BWB Texts

Short books on big subjects
from great New Zealand writers

Pesticides and Health
How New Zealand Fails
in Environmental Protection

NEIL PEARCE

Contents

Dedicated to my friends and colleagues at the Massey University Centre for Public Health Research, who successfully completed these studies under very difficult circumstances – and to my brother Paul who passed away in Levin while I was writing this, stuck on the other side of the world.

1. A Tale of Two Pandemics

I had just started writing this book in London when the pandemic struck. For more than a year, like many other epidemiologists, I was diverted into work on Covid-19, and during that year I watched from afar, with growing pride and admiration, New Zealand's world-leading pandemic response. It wasn't perfect (how could it be?), but it was light years ahead of the response in other Western countries, and equal to, or better than, those in the Asia-Pacific countries that handled the pandemic well. My frustration at not being 'at home' was increased by the inept response of most European countries. Hubris and European exceptionalism dominated, and there was a remarkable unwillingness to learn from the success stories from the Asia-Pacific region.

Like most other Western countries, New Zealand was ill-prepared to handle a pandemic. However, it has a long history of successful public health action, a high level of scientific activity and, most importantly, world-class scientists, policymakers and politicians – as shown by their willingness to admit that they didn't know everything and to learn from the actions of other nations. Moreover, they had the courage of their convictions, and the wisdom and energy to see things through.

This is all the more remarkable given New Zealand's abysmal history in environmental protection. In a small country like New Zealand, a handful of individual scientists, policymakers and journalists can often tip the balance, and New Zealand's failures in safeguarding the environment can in part be attributed to a small number of such individuals, but these failures are also structural, and have been a long time in the making. In this book I'm going to focus on New Zealand's dismal history of pesticide mismanagement – in particular, the problem of dioxin. However, I will argue that this provides a case study of how we fail in environmental protection overall.

I have been closely involved in studies of the health effects of dioxin, and pesticides more generally, since 1981. This has included studying the workers at the Ivon Watkins-Dow (IWD) plant at New Plymouth and timber treatment workers exposed to pentachlorophenol (PCP) in Bay of Plenty, as well as a chaotic visit to Vietnam with a US committee investigating the health effects of Agent Orange on Vietnam veterans and the Vietnamese themselves. In the following chapters I discuss various attempts by corporations to 'manage' research into dioxin by hiring consultants to dispute the decisions of regulatory bodies. Government agencies tried not to get involved, or even sided with the companies against the research of independent bodies such as the World Health Organization (WHO), and against university-based researchers such as myself.

So where does the 'tale of two pandemics' (the title of this chapter) come in? Clearly, we have been having a pandemic of deaths and long-term illness from Covid-19. Ill health from pesticide exposure is not a pandemic in the classic sense, but in people with heavy pesticide exposure the risks are comparable. If a middle-aged person got Covid-19 at the beginning (pre-vaccination) of the pandemic, they had about a 1 per cent chance of dying in the next month, and it would be fairly obvious that they had died from Covid-19. If a person has had heavy pesticide exposure (particularly if it contains some type of dioxin) they too have a 1 per cent chance of dying as a result (usually from cancer but also from some other diseases, such as diabetes).[1] However, it would be many years after the exposure occurred and probably no one would make the connection. This is why the health effects of pesticides are so hard to research – you need epidemiological studies comparing large numbers of 'exposed' and 'non-exposed' people who are followed over a long period of time.

Covid-19 serves as a model of how science works, and doesn't work, but it has all happened in fast forward. Imagine how the events of the past few years would look if spread over the past sixty years like the pesticide controversies. There are initial concerns but not much hard evidence; there is confusion and disagreement among scientists; policymakers are reluctant to change their policies until there is clear evidence; the resulting confusion may create a lack of trust between some sections of the community and the policymakers and scientists. When there is a lack of trust, conspiracy theories thrive. I will return to all these issues in the last chapter, but first I have a few personal stories to tell.

2. Vietnam

It was May 1995, twenty years after the end of the Vietnam War, and the American embargo against Vietnam had just ended. I was the only non-American on the first official US visit there, with a committee that had been sent by Congress to investigate the possibility of studying the health effects of Agent Orange. Agent Orange was a mixture of two pesticides – 2,4-dichlorophenoxyacetic acid (2,4-D) and 2,4,5-trichlorophenoxyacetic acid (2,4,5-T) – both of which had been used in Western countries (in fact 2,4-D still is). Contaminated by dioxin (2,3,7,8-tetrachlorodibenzo-para-dioxin (TCDD)) in very high levels – see the appendix for a brief primer on what dioxin is, and what it does – the mixture had been sprayed extensively in Vietnam as part of the war, with the aim of defoliating forests so that the Americans and their allies could more easily observe enemy troop movements and supply lines.

For several decades there had been reports of birth defects and cancer cases among both the Vietnamese and the US and other troops who had sprayed the chemicals or had been sprayed themselves. The US research agencies had already funded several studies of the US troops, with strong lobbying from the veterans to do more.

I had demonstrated against the Vietnam War when I was at university in the early 1970s and had always been fascinated by the story of Agent Orange. So, when I received the invitation to visit Vietnam, I immediately accepted. I then got a letter from the US National Institute of Environmental Health Sciences (NIEHS) informing me that there would be a 'fact-finding' visit to Ho Chi Minh City (Saigon) in the south of Vietnam, and a pesticide epidemiology workshop in Hanoi in the north. The director of Vietnam's National Institute of Occupational and Environmental Health (NIOEH) also invited me to the workshop. It was made clear in correspondence from NIOEH that the fact-finding mission in the south was specifically to focus on the health effects of Agent Orange/dioxin exposure, and that these issues would also be considered at the more general workshop on pesticides in Hanoi.

Arriving in Ho Chi Minh City on a steamy tropical evening, I took a rickshaw to the hotel in an old part of the city. From my hotel window, I could see giant rats scurrying along an open sewer. I made my way down to the hotel bar where I met the other members of the delegation and had my first Vietnamese Tiger beer. It was only then that I discovered I was a member of an official US delegation, and that the visit had been requested by Congress. Moreover, this was the first official visit to Vietnam by a US government group since the twenty-year embargo on contact with the country had been dropped a few months earlier. It seems that American Vietnam veterans had been lobbying for more studies on the health effects of Agent Orange and had successfully pressured Congress to fund them. Many such studies were already being done on US citizens, so now Congress was looking to fund studies in Vietnam on the effects on the Vietnamese themselves. The motive was mostly to help the US veterans rather than the Vietnamese.

I had not been informed of this goal before arriving in Vietnam, either officially or unofficially. In a subsequent report I argued that, if I had been, I would not have agreed to participate, since I felt that there were important ethical issues involved in scientists from one country conducting studies in another country for the purpose of benefitting only their own citizens rather than the population under study. These ethical issues were compounded by an order of magnitude in the case of Agent Orange studies in Vietnam, since it was US army personnel that exposed the Vietnamese population (as well as US troops) to this potential hazard.

The 10-80 Committee

The next day we met with the 10-80 Committee to Study the Consequences of Chemicals Used during Wartime (10-80 Committee), a Vietnamese network of researchers into the health effects of Agent Orange. Founded in October 1980 (hence the name), it was based at the Hanoi Medical School with local committees throughout Vietnam.[1] The war had finished in 1975, but it was five years before the committee was formed. However, it seems that there was little support from the government for its work – the country had more pressing problems to deal with than Agent Orange – and there was little international help, particularly because of the US embargo.

The 10-80 Committee was headed by Professor Hoàng Đình Cầu, who had been a deputy of Hồ Chí Minh and had fought in the war. He spoke only Vietnamese and French, and only I and one other member of the committee spoke French, so we travelled around with Professor Cầu for the next two days, hearing his stories about the war and Agent Orange.

We were first taken to the former Ho Chi Minh Trail to see the devastation of the tropical forest still evident some twenty years after the war had ended and twenty-four years after the spraying had stopped. Very little was growing there – only a few plants and virtually no forest. Some thought it was because of the dioxin in the soil, whereas others said that when you destroy tropical rainforest (by any means) it takes hundreds of years to grow back. Whatever the explanation, the area was barely habitable, and in fact resettlement had only begun a few months before. I met one family, living in a traditional house with a thatched roof, who had moved there from the north only a few months before. They were growing their own food and taking water from the river.

When we arrived back at the Từ Dũ Obstetrics and Gynaecology Hospital in Ho Chi Minh City, Vietnamese television was filming our arrival and our reactions as we were shown into a room full of shelves and jars. In the jars were deformed foetuses and babies. There must have been about a hundred or more of them, and we were told that more were being added all the time. We were also shown evidence of a number of cases of choriocarcinoma (cancer of the placenta) in young women. It was powerful and overwhelming. These were horrible deformities. The scene was described in an article in *The Guardian*:

> The science of chemical warfare fills a silent white tiled room at Tu Du Hospital in Ho Chi Minh City. Here, shelves are overburdened with research materials. Behind the locked door is an iridescent wall of the mutated and misshapen, hundreds of bell jars and vacuum-sealed bottles in which human foetuses float in formaldehyde. Some appear to be sleeping, fingers curling their hair, thumbs pressing at their lips, while others with multiple heads and mangled limbs are listless and slumped. Thankfully, none of these dioxin babies ever woke up. One floor below, it is never quiet. Here are those who have survived the misery of birth, ravaged infants whom no one has the ability to understand, babies so traumatized by their own disabilities, luckless children so enraged and depressed at their miserable fate, that they are tied to their beds just to keep them safe from harm.[2]

In fact, many serious birth defects look striking and distressing (no matter how they are caused), and about 2–3 per cent of all births (even in New Zealand) involve congenital malformations – some minor, some serious. If you went into any regional hospital in New Zealand and started recording all the spontaneous abortions and babies who died soon after birth, you would fairly soon have a list of various deformities. So what does this prove? It proves that deformities are happening. It doesn't tell you anything about whether they are happening more in one part of the country than in another, whether they have become more or less frequent, or whether they are linked with particular exposures. To find this out, you need to do an epidemiological study, comparing the proportions of babies born with birth defects in different parts of the country, or in the families of those exposed and not exposed to Agent Orange.

So it was impossible to know from these tragic case reports (and displays) whether they were linked to Agent Orange. However, the local doctors were clearly concerned and, during our discussions, said that these two health problems (birth defects and choriocarcinoma) were their first two priorities for study. We sat down and began to discuss how studies could be done. It would be very difficult because of the length of time that had passed since the spraying had stopped in 1971 – but it was not impossible.

A number of studies had already measured population exposure to TCDD and other dioxins in various parts of Vietnam. Work was under way on conducting such studies on a larger scale and producing a 'dioxin map' of the southern part of the country. With this it would be possible to estimate a person's exposure based on their areas of residence and their activities. This work was already being done by an epidemiologist at the 10-80 Committee, using available US records of spraying operations. So, we could develop a study of 'cases' of birth defects and 'controls' (normal births) in relation to the mother's estimated exposure, based on where she had lived before and during the pregnancy.

At this point we were interrupted by another member

of our visiting committee, the representative of the US Veterans Administration (now the US Department of Veterans Affairs), who said that they were not interested in studies of health problems in women, since they were not relevant to US veterans (almost all of whom are men), and that Congress was therefore unlikely to fund them. In other words, we were wasting our time. It was stunning to think that health problems among these women could just be ignored.

This put our visiting committee in a crisis. We decided that, as individuals, we had such different attitudes and agendas that it would be futile to try and produce a single report on which we could all agree. There were eight of us, so we would do eight separate reports. In mine, I said the attitudes of some committee members were 'insensitive to say the least'.[3] I subsequently discovered that the mandate from the US Senate had not been so restrictive: in fact, it discussed the need to 'facilitate further research on the health effects of Agent Orange and other herbicides on American veterans and others' and to 'determine the types of collaborations amenable to Vietnamese scientists and the degree to which these studies might benefit the Vietnamese people and the people of the United States'. I should stress that the leader of the delegation (Dr Christopher Portier, NIEHS) did an excellent job in extremely difficult circumstances. The problem was the restrictive way in which some members of the delegation interpreted the Senate mandate. This was difficult, but things were about to get worse.

The National Institute of Environmental Health Sciences

We headed north to Hanoi in an aging Vietnam Airlines plane. Hanoi was beautiful, an old colonial French city with almost no modern buildings. The Second World War, the French war, the American war and then the American embargo had ensured that no modern industry or modern office buildings were constructed. This was just beginning to change, but Hanoi still had the air of 1930s Asia and Somerset Maugham.

That evening we met with the director of Vietnam's NIOEH, who was hosting us in Hanoi. He told us that we were not allowed to discuss dioxin during our visit, and that we should remove any slides about it from our talks for the symposium that was to take place over the next two days. The symposium was to be about pesticides, not dioxin. Since all of us were experts in dioxin, and almost all our slides were about it, this didn't leave us with much to talk about. The tense situation was made worse when one member of our visiting committee argued with the director that 'we have been sent here by our Congress to talk about doing studies of dioxin, and our government will be very angry with your government if we are not allowed to talk about them'.

In the end we conceded defeat, and the next two days were spent in a bizarre symposium where everyone managed to talk about dioxin without using the word, and without showing any slides about dioxin. Christopher Portier got the gathering off to a great start with a twenty-minute overview of pesticides and health. His first slide (these were the days before PowerPoint) was upside down, so the operator of the projector turned it the right way up but got it back-to-front. There are eight possible ways of putting a slide into a projector, one right and seven wrong, and the operator cycled through the seven wrong ones for the next twenty minutes while Chris completed his talk without even managing to show his first slide. So at least he didn't show any slides about dioxin. We then had an early break for morning tea, while the audiovisual people had an emergency meeting to work out which way to put the slides into the machine.

For the next four days, the 10-80 Committee and the NIOEH competed for our time. There were constant disagreements about who we were meeting, and who would take us for lunch or dinner. Two competing points of view – those of the committee and the NIOEH – became apparent. The latter was allied to a faction within the government that wanted to promote Vietnam as a rice-exporting nation and feared the effect on sales if people believed the rice to be contaminated with dioxin. So the NIOEH faction didn't want Agent Orange studies done, and the 10-80 Committee did. The NIOEH faction held greater sway in Hanoi so we only managed to meet twice briefly with the committee.

Heading to the airport, we were exhausted and keen to get out. The government officials people looked agitated as soon as we walked into the terminal, and when we presented our passports we were all taken aside, one by one. I was led into a windowless room where they went through all my papers and slides and confiscated everything the 10-80 Committee had given us. Then they let me go, and I began to think that I might see

New Zealand again after all. Eventually I made it onto the plane (Vietnam Airlines), where I reunited with the rest of our committee, all of whom had had the same experience. As I settled back into my seat and we pulled away from the terminal building, I started to relax. Then the safety announcement began, with two crew members up front giving the announcements and a third member down the back (where we were all seated) throwing up into the toilet. I decided not to eat the airline food.

The incident at the airport was reported in *Science*:

> On 30 June, customs officials at Hanoi airport seized most of the research material collected during the trip, which explored potential collaborations to trace the impact on the population of Agent Orange … The visiting researchers were given no reason for the seizure, although there are rumours that the incident reflects a feeling among some government officials that pursuing the matter – regardless of its potential scientific value – could jeopardize future ties with the United States … The officials seized a range of materials, including 40 blood samples from people exposed to Agent Orange in Laos, 26 samples of Vietnamese food – such as milk, fish and beef – destined for a lab in Amsterdam, Netherlands, to be analysed for dioxin, and scientific papers and other documents prepared by Vietnamese officials.[4]

The seizure of the materials became a diplomatic incident between the US and Vietnamese governments. The US scientists did not return for another eight years, by which time it was definitely too late, if it had not been already, to do studies.

So what is known about the health effects on the Vietnamese of Agent Orange exposure? Plenty of studies show that dioxin exposure occurred, but very few have shown the health effects of such exposure (such as cancer or birth defects, for instance). The studies that were needed mostly didn't get done, initially because of the US embargo and subsequently because of obstruction from the Vietnamese government itself. However, even in more recent years the US government has not encouraged studies to be done. An article in the magazine *Mother Jones* reported:

For the State Department, the question of how to respond to Vietnam's concerns over Agent Orange is an explosive one – especially for the U.S. embassy in Hanoi which handles Agent Orange inquiries as if they were poison. 'It's a very, very sensitive issue'... In Washington, a State Department official speaking on background was far more frank ... 'for us there is a real concern that if we start down the road of research, what does that portend for liability-type issues further on'. Vietnam certainly has its own reasons to avoid pushing the issue too aggressively. Given the decades of war and mutual suspicion between Washington and Hanoi, it's not surprising that many Vietnamese don't trust the United States, and those feelings are complicated by Vietnam's worries that tourism and food exports could suffer if the world perceives that Vietnam is widely contaminated with TCDD ... Hanoi also deals gingerly with the Agent Orange issue because it places a high priority on commercial ties with the United States and on advancing trade talks.[5]

Vietnam veterans

Most of what we know, then, about the health effects of Agent Orange in Vietnam comes from studies of US and Australian troops (some of whom were spraying the chemicals) rather than of the Vietnamese themselves. Apart from the injustice of this, it also leads to considerable scientific problems, since most of the troops would have had much lower exposure than the Vietnamese; the troops were only there for a couple of years and (mostly) were not directly sprayed, whereas the Vietnamese were deliberately sprayed and had to keep living there. Also, the troops were almost entirely adult men, so studies of them tell us little about the effects of exposures in women or children.

So, what have the studies of US and Australian veterans shown? The best summary is provided in a report by the US Committee to Review the Health Effects in Vietnam Veterans of Exposure to Herbicides, first published in 1994 and updated regularly since. It shows that most of the numerous studies have been hampered by relatively poor measures of exposure to herbicides or TCDD, as well as some other methodological problems. Most of the TCDD evidence comes from studies of people exposed to dioxin or herbicides in occupational and environmental settings (more on this later) rather than from studies of Vietnam veterans. Many studies have merely used 'service in Vietnam' as a surrogate measure of exposure

('VAO committees have treated Vietnam-veteran status as a proxy for herbicide exposure'), assuming that everyone who served there was exposed to Agent Orange.[6] Although that is probably true, for many of them the level of exposure would have been very low. However, once you try and find out which troops had more exposure and which had less, things quickly become very confused.

Nevertheless, the various forms of the committee over the years have managed to piece together useful evidence from various sources (an approach that I will discuss more later), particularly from occupational studies, and have been able to reach conclusions on the main health effects of Agent Orange exposure. The most recent (2018) version of the committee's report lists soft-tissue sarcoma, non-Hodgkin's lymphoma, chronic lymphocytic leukemia, Hodgkin's lymphoma, hypertension and monoclonal gammopathy of undetermined significance (MGUS) as conditions with sufficient evidence of an association with Agent Orange exposure.[7] There is a longer list of diseases (laryngeal cancer, lung cancer, prostate cancer, bladder cancer, multiple myeloma, AL amyloidosis, early-onset peripheral neuropathy, Parkinson's disease, porphyria cutanea tarda, ischaemic heart disease, stroke and hypothyroidism) with 'limited or suggestive evidence of an association'. The International Agency for Research on Cancer (IARC) has also classified TCDD as a human carcinogen, and has concluded that, unusually, it increases the risk of cancer in general, not just some specific types of cancer.[8]

New Zealand Vietnam veterans

Most of the US and Australian troops who went to Vietnam were conscripted. New Zealand's troops, on the other hand, were volunteers, and the numbers were small. Initially only twenty-two army engineers went there in 1964, but in May 1965 an artillery battery was also sent, and combat began in Biên Hòa province in July. Other units deployed at various times included a medical team, an SAS unit, and navy and air force personnel. Overall, 3,368 New Zealand men and women served in Vietnam.[9]

In 1990 I applied to the War Pensions Medical Research Trust and the Health Research Council (HRC) for funding for a study of mortality and cancer incidence (the number of new cases of cancer each year) in New Zealand Vietnam veterans. The application was supported by the Vietnam Veterans Association of New Zealand, although they did say that they would also like to see a study of the health and welfare of Vietnam veterans' children. I acknowledged in the application that the proposed study was 'limited by the relatively small number of Vietnam veterans' and that there was 'little chance of detecting an increased risk of a specific rare cancer', but that 'study power is adequate for examining mortality from all causes, and overall cancer mortality and incidence'. However, both agencies rejected the application on the basis that the numbers were too small and that the exposure data was inadequate. Although these criticisms had some validity, they ignored the major concerns among Vietnam veterans that their friends were dying. The study wouldn't have been able to detect an increased risk of a rare cancer (such as soft-tissue sarcoma), but it would have been able to detect an elevated overall death rate, or overall cancer rate. Thus, it might not have contributed much scientifically to the dioxin and specific disease issue (given that larger studies were already being done in the US and Australia), but it certainly would have provided some useful information for New Zealand Vietnam veterans.

So, what do we know about the health effects of Agent Orange in New Zealand Vietnam veterans? We have three government reports.

The Reeves Report

The Reeves Report on the health status of children of Vietnam and Operation Grapple veterans was funded by the government and compiled in 1998–99.[10] Operation Grapple was the British series of nine atmospheric nuclear weapons tests on Christmas and Malden islands in 1957–58. New Zealand sent three ships to the tests, and there has been continuing controversy ever since, as with Vietnam veterans, as to whether crew members' health – and their children's health – suffered as a result.

Operation Grapple and Agent Orange represented similar political problems for the government. Both involve former service personnel who had received an exposure that they believed had affected their health and the health of their children. In both instances, there were issues regarding the responsibilities of the Defence Force towards former personnel and their families, and their needs for health care and continued monitoring. Politically it made sense to consider the two sets of issues

24

together, but scientifically it made no sense at all. These were two quite different exposures, and there was no reason to believe that just because one group had (or had not) experienced specific health problems, the same would apply to the other group.

The Reeves Report focused on the children of personnel who had served in Vietnam or at the Christmas Island tests. It concluded that 'our investigations do not convincingly demonstrate any causal connection between exposures to service personnel and health effects in their children ... with the possible exception of spina bifida ... the current state of science and medical knowledge does not point to a link between exposure ... to defoliants, herbicides and pesticides and the health of their children'. Crucially, the report concluded that 'there is only one recorded case of possible exposure of ANZAC troops to aerially delivered Agent Orange ... It is known that New Zealand troops operated in areas that had been subject to previous defoliation but they were not in those areas at or near the time of defoliation.' In other words, they had not been exposed, so any health problems they had could not be due to Agent Orange.

The McLeod Report

Following the Reeves Report, Veterans Affairs commissioned the Wellington School of Medicine to produce a research report. This subsequently became known as the McLeod Report.[11] Like the Reeves one, it started with the statement that the New Zealand troops had not been exposed: '[T]he information available to the authors was that ANZAC forces generally served in Phuoc Tuy province where there was no aerial spraying'. This assumption, which was later found to be wrong, unfortunately coloured the whole report, and the reaction to its publication in August 2001. The bulk of the report involved a detailed review of studies done in other populations, particularly in children of US Vietnam veterans. Relatively few studies had been done, and the authors of the McLeod Report were largely very critical of them, finding them so flawed that no firm conclusions could be drawn. My own feeling was that many of the criticisms had some validity, but that it was wrong to dismiss the studies altogether.

It's impossible to do a perfect study of such a complex issue, and there will always be problems of small numbers, inaccurate exposure data and misclassification of disease. However, epidemiologists have generally become adept at assessing these possible types of bias as to how serious they may be and in what direction they may operate. A study cannot be dismissed simply because there may be some inaccuracies in the data, but this is what the McLeod Report's authors tended to do. However, although I didn't agree with everything in the report, and I considered it to be quite conservative in its assessment of the published studies, nevertheless its conclusions were within the 'normal range' of such reports.

The Parliamentary Inquiry

The *Inquiry into the Exposure of New Zealand Defence Personnel to Agent Orange and Other Defoliant Chemicals during the Vietnam War and Any Health Effects of That Exposure* was presented to Parliament by the chair of its Health Committee in October 2004.[12] The inquiry was quite specifically set up to consider the Reeves and McLeod reports, but was also prompted by the emergence in April 2003 of new evidence that New Zealand Vietnam veterans had in fact been exposed to Agent Orange. The new evidence included a map provided by the former commander of 161 Battery, given to him by the US Defense Force in Vietnam, that identified areas of chemical defoliation, 'including the Nui Dat area, in Phuoc Tuy province, where New Zealand defence personnel were based'. Clearly, the authors of the McLeod Report had been naïve in accepting the assurance of Veterans Affairs that the veterans had not been exposed to Agent Orange, particularly when so many veterans were telling stories of having been sprayed with it. They should at least have quoted the accounts of veterans who told a different story. However, they perhaps did not deserve the fate that awaited them at the hands of the parliamentary committee.

The committee strongly criticised them for accepting the assurances of Veterans Affairs, without saying how they could have done otherwise given the limited funding and time available for preparing their report. It faulted them for not accurately representing the literature – in particular Australian studies that found an increase in suicide rates in children of Vietnam veterans. It pointed out that, in terms of the children of US and Australian Vietnam veterans, the following effects are also accepted: spina bifida, cleft lip/palate, adrenal gland cancer and birth defects in the children of female veterans. 'The McLeod Report', the committee concluded, 'makes a fundamentally incorrect assumption by stating that New Zealand defence forces were not exposed to herbicides', and this had biased the authors' interpretation of the substantive data and 'discredited the report in the eyes of many readers'.[13]

So where does this leave us with Agent Orange and New Zealand troops? Some would argue that they had little or no exposure; others would argue that they did have significant exposure and are likely to have also had some resulting health effects. In any case, in 2014 they received an official Crown apology from the government, stating:

For too long, successive governments ignored concerns being raised by Viet Nam veterans. It was the emergence of Agent Orange as a serious health and veterans' issue in the United States which began to change the way in which issues surrounding Viet Nam veterans came to be perceived and then treated in New Zealand.

In 2003 the Health Select Committee undertook its own inquiry into the concerns raised by veterans. It investigated whether New Zealand defence personnel had been exposed to Agent Orange. It also assessed the health risks to defence personnel and their families, and the health services available to them. The Committee concluded that New Zealand personnel who had served in Viet Nam had indeed been exposed to Agent Orange, and that this exposure had had adverse health effects not only for the personnel themselves, but also for their children.[14]

3. Bringing It All Back Home

So, who was producing these toxic chemicals with which the New Zealand troops were sprayed? At least some were made in New Plymouth. The New Zealand firm of Ivon Watkins was created in 1946 and began production of 2,4,5-T in 1948. The operation was based at several sites around New Plymouth, but in 1960 these were centralised at a new factory in the suburb of Paritutū. In 1965 the US company Dow Chemical purchased a share of Ivon Watkins and it became known as Ivon Watkins-Dow (IWD); in 1988 Dow bought the company outright, and it became known as Dow Elanco in 1991, and subsequently Dow AgroSciences.[1]

For twenty-one years until 1969, the company imported 2,4,5-trichlorophenol (TCP) from overseas and only carried out the second stage of the production process – that is, turning TCP into 2,4,5-T. After 1969 the company started manufacturing TCP itself at the Paritutū plant. Since the dioxin contaminant is produced at the first stage (the manufacture of TCP), it is reasonable to assume that there would have been relatively low exposure to the workforce and the surrounding community up until 1969. After that, the workers' exposure likely increased markedly.

The most intense exposures, both to the workers and the surrounding community, are likely to have occurred between 1969 and 1974 when the Clean Air Act (passed in 1972) began to take effect (more on this later). However, production of 2,4,5-T continued until 1987, and in the 1980s the factory was one of the last (perhaps the last) in the world still producing 2,4,5-T.[2]

One continuing controversy was whether the Paritutū plant had been producing Agent Orange. It had produced both 2,4,5-T and 2,4-D, which can be mixed together to make Agent Orange, and had exported some of these products. I know of no evidence that the two chemicals were deliberately combined to make Agent Orange in New Zealand, but it is quite possible the company knew these were combined for that purpose after being exported.

It was denied for many years that the factory had produced Agent Orange, and a parliamentary select committee inquiry held in 1990, under a Labour government, concluded that 'no conclusive facts or evidence were provided to the Committee to substantiate the claim that IWD manufactured the formation of Agent Orange during the Vietnam War'. Only in 2005 did the next Labour government concede that the factory had in fact been manufacturing the two components of Agent Orange. Transport Minister Harry Duynhoven told the *Sunday News*, 'the information that has been given to me is that products used to make Agent Orange were shipped from New Plymouth to Subic Bay in the Philippines'.

A subsequent magazine report quoted an anonymous former top official at IWD:

I was on the management committee of Ivon Watkins Dow, and I supported the plan to export Agent Orange. In fact, it went ahead on my casting vote. People who'd served in the armed forces made a strong case for the need to defoliate the jungle, because of the risk to servicemen from ambush or sniper fire from the undergrowth. So we began manufacturing this Agent Orange, but it didn't meet the international specifications and probably had an excess of 'nasties' in it. The problem was, we didn't consider the product was harmful to humans at the time. Our scientists relied on assurances and technical data provided to them by Dow Chemicals in the USA. We were led to believe it was safe. The whole reason I supported Agent Orange is because we thought that we were giving our boys on the ground a hand.[3]

So, if 2,4,5-T and other chemicals were being manufactured at the Paritutū plant, what was happening to the waste? This was a question I asked several times when I visited the plant in the early 1980s – I wanted to include the plant in a larger international study organised by the WHO's IARC. I should stress that the company – at that time it was called Ivon Watkins-Dow – was generally quite helpful, and I appreciated its willingness to cooperate with the study.

Before 1969 there would have been relatively little waste containing dioxin, given that the TCP was imported until then. After 1969, however, 'dioxin was likely released in air and liquid waste as a contaminant or byproduct in the local manufacturing process'.[4] I had been told by colleagues that in earlier years the disposal of waste was very lax, but that things tightened up following the passing of the Clean Air Act 1972.

From 1973, solvents were used to reduce the dioxin levels in the 2,4,5-T from about 1 part per million (ppm) to about 0.005 ppm. The solvents were then stored and burned in a liquid-waste incinerator onsite between 1975 and 1979.[5] From 1978, a new process was introduced to further reduce the dioxin levels – it's not clear what this was but it probably involved filtering the TCP through charcoal. Usually the solid charcoal waste containing the dioxin would then be stored, and later (perhaps from 1980) burned in a solid-incinerator.[6] If this process was followed it would eliminate 99.9 per cent of the dioxin; a small amount would still be emitted from the chimney of the incinerator and fall on the surrounding area.

These changes were presumably introduced as a result of the Clean Air Act 1972, in accordance with which the Department of Scientific and Industrial Research (DSIR) monitored incinerator emissions from 1974 to 1979, and again from 1983 to 1986.[7] The New Plymouth City Council first issued a licence to IWD in 1974; before that, there were no reported regulations or monitoring of industry emissions. 'Other factors such as fugitive emissions of unknown quantity and the lack of data on dioxin contaminants in various production materials make exposures difficult to accurately assess.'[8] Thus, 1969 to 1974 is likely to have been the peak period for dioxin contamination in the surrounding community.

When I first visited the plant in 1982, I asked whether the waste was being incinerated and was told several times that 'it's commercially sensitive, but I can assure you that no waste is incinerated and none leaves the plant'. At the next visit I would ask the same question and get the same answer.

I never found out what really happened, but I have heard two versions of the story. One is simply that the waste *was* being incinerated and therefore the answer I received was wrong.[9] The other is that what I was told was right: the waste was *not* being incinerated, and not leaving the plant – it was simply being put into barrels and dumped onsite.

The same anonymous IWD official was quoted as saying that the latter had certainly happened in the 1970s:

> The company owned a large piece of land 'very close to the chemical plant, which we called "the Experimental Farm". We bulldozed big pits and dumped thousands of tonnes of chemicals there … I remember at one meeting … that there was some real concern expressed about the chemical dump. "If it leaches down onto the beach, we're going to be in real trouble."'[10]

A participant in our subsequent study (see below) even reported to us that he and his friends had played in the drums when they were children!

The issue of what had happened to the waste was still very much alive as I was completing this book. A \$3 million operation to remove dioxin from the sludge at the New Plymouth waste water treatment plant had raised questions about where the dioxin had come from, with the former IWD plant (now called Corteva) a prime suspect. This in turn has raised questions about what other historical dump sites may have been contaminated.[11]

An accident at the factory in 1972 resulted in a fire and a mushroom cloud explosion in the butanoic acid plant, but this apparently did not involve dioxin. In 1974, waste from manufacturing was buried at the IWD farm site at Ngahoro, and there was a similar disposal in 1976 at the company's Waihoro research farm.[12] The incinerator was installed in 1982. In 1986, however, an explosion in the TCP manufacturing plant caused by the failure of an incorrectly installed rupture disc assembly, resulted in a release of TCP into the air.[13] This led to a ministerial committee of inquiry, which reported in October 1986, and production of 2,4,5-T ceased the following year.[14] The committee noted that New Zealand was perhaps the last country in the world producing 2,4,5-T, and one of the last to be using it. At the time, it had been banned in Argentina, Sweden, Italy and Mexico, and was no longer used in Brazil, France, Canada, West Germany and the UK. The only country to which New Zealand had been exporting 2,4,5-T directly was Australia; some had been exported to Malaysia in the past, and a product containing 2,4,5-T was exported to Fiji.

So what was happening in the neighbourhood? When the Paritutū factory was built in 1960 there was no housing nearby, but housing development was subsequently approved by the local authorities.[15]

From the 1960s on, community groups had raised concerns about airborne emissions, odours and health effects. As Virginia Baker of Environmental Science and

34

Research (ESR) notes: 'Some members of the community were very angry as the issue had been simmering since the 1960s. Some people perceived that the government had not adequately responded to their concerns for many years.'[16]

As in Vietnam, there were plenty of anecdotes and case reports, particularly about birth defects and cancer, as well as some reports of cases of multiple sclerosis.[17] The *New Zealand Herald* reported:

> Former midwife Hyacinth Henderson, aged 87, and now living in Dunedin, says she saw many birth defects when she worked at New Plymouth's Westown Maternity Hospital. Between 1965 and 1971 she recorded 167 birth defects out of 5392 babies born there ... they had abnormalities she had never seen before and she had been in obstetrics for 40 years. 'Some of them were horrific ... There were two anencephalics, which means there is no brain or the brain is sheared off above the eyebrows. There were a large number of bone deformities such as clubbed feet and things like that.'[18]

On the other hand, in 2001 the local Medical Officer of Health, Patrick O'Connor, reported no excess of cancer registrations, and actually a lower than expected rate of birth defect notifications.[19] Cancer deaths were in excess (ninety-one over ten years compared with eighty-six expected), but the small difference made it difficult to draw conclusions. In 2005 the Ministry of Health (MoH) drew similar conclusions.[20] In contrast, one of the community activists disputed the claim that dioxin was relatively harmless, and argued that the reports were misleading, particularly because they examined cancer and birth defect rates in the wider area, rather than in the smaller group of people who received significant exposure.[21]

The first ESR report

After several decades of requests from Paritutū residents, in 2001 MoH finally agreed to fund a survey of dioxin levels in the community.[22] It contracted ESR to do a blood survey, and also to test the soil. ESR is a Crown research institute (many were created out of the old DSIR) specialising in testing and research for environmental exposures.

The blood (serum) study eventually involved testing fifty-two residents of the area – twenty-four in the first round and twenty-eight in the second – chosen from 831 volunteers who had responded to advertisements. The study was restricted to people who had lived in Paritutū but not worked in the factory. This was partly because the study had arisen out of residents' concerns about environmental contamination, but also because the workers were the responsibility of the Occupational Safety and Health (OSH) service of the Department of Labour (DoL), whereas the residents (and the public in general) were the responsibility of MoH, which was funding the survey.

In its report on the results of the first round of blood testing in February 2004, ESR stated that 'a statistically significant elevation in serum TCDD compared to national TCDD serum concentrations was found in the study group.

The mean serum TCDD level for the group was 10.8 pg/g [picograms per gram] lipid, while the expected national mean for a similar group was 3.5 pg/g.'[23]

In other words, the residents had blood levels of dioxin about three times the national average for people of the same age. The authors concluded:

> [T]hese findings support the premise that aerial emissions containing TCDD were responsible for the soil and serum dioxin concentrations in Paritutū. Dioxin profiles in the Paritutū environment, its residents and the measured TCDD elevations are most likely not a result of combustion processes, such as incineration. Whether these emissions were a result of regular or more episodic releases cannot be determined by the current study.[24]

Before the first-round report was published, I received a visit from David Phillips, who was head of the ESR group doing the survey and a co-author of the report. MoH was stunned by the results and did not want to release them. Officials had apparently argued that these were only preliminary results and should not be made public until the second round had been completed.

This was madness. The results were dynamite and ethically could not possibly be kept secret for six months while the second round of testing was done. In any case, they were bound to leak. And what was MoH, and ESR, supposed to say over the next six months as the public kept asking for the first-round results?

I suggested to David that he arrange for the draft report to be reviewed, and I volunteered as a reviewer.

My review said the findings should be made public as soon as possible; a second reviewer, from overseas, also said the report should be 'released as soon as possible before it leaks'. Armed with these reviews, ESR went back to the ministry, which finally agreed to make the findings public.

The release was scheduled for the morning of 9 September 2004, but the report leaked and the findings were published in the *New Zealand Herald* earlier that same morning:

> A report on the effects of exposure to dioxin from Ivon Watkins-Dow's chemical plant is today expected to overturn 30 years of assurances that residents had nothing to fear. The residents have claimed for years that the plant's emissions caused birth defects, cancer and other diseases ... The Herald understands the study out today reveals a serious public health problem and will contradict previous assurances that residents had little to fear from dioxin exposure.[25]

The *Herald* story originally included a timeline of 'how it happened':

1948:   IWD starts making 2,4,5-T in New Plymouth.
1960:   IWD moves to Paritutū.
1965:   Midwife Hyacinth Henderson tells Health Department officials of 'horrific' deformities in newborn babies.
1971:   Miss Henderson records 167 birth defects out of 5,392 babies born at Westown Hospital 1965–71. Health Department does nothing.

1983: Dow stops making 2,4,5-T in the US.

1986: Committee of inquiry finds no proof that 2,4,5-T has any ill effects on New Plymouth residents' health.

1987: IWD stops making 2,4,5-T in New Plymouth.

1999: New Plymouth residents find 'serious illnesses' in 100 of 183 Paritutū families.

2001–2: Taranaki Medical Officer of Health Patrick O'Connor finds that birth defects and cancers in Paritutū area are statistically the same as the national average.

2002: Ministry for the Environment finds soil dioxin at one site near Paritutū is twice the recommended guideline, but a 'negligible' health risk to residents.

2004: ESR is believed to have found high dioxin levels in the blood of Paritutū residents.

What about the workers?

I appeared on television as a commentator on the report and what MoH was doing (the ministry had suggested me as a neutral commentator):

A Massey University epidemiologist who has made several studies of the weedkiller 2,4,5-T, Professor Neil Pearce, said yesterday it was 'bizarre' that the Ministry of Health had arranged special help for the Paritutū community when nothing had been done for the Ivon Watkins-Dow workers. 'We don't have production worker [dioxin] figures for New Zealand, but my guess is that they would be at least 10 times what we are seeing in the community,' he said. 'You have the bizarre situation where there is quite a lot being done to help the community and nothing being done to help the workers who had the highest exposures.'[26]

The 'bizarre situation' was occurring because, as noted earlier, the workers were the responsibility of the OSH section of the DoL. An MoH spokesperson appeared on television saying that the workers were not their responsibility, only the community members were. OSH also issued a press statement saying the workers were not its responsibility because the exposures predated its creation in 1992. It seemed that the workers were no one's responsibility.

The second ESR report

ESR issued its report on both rounds of testing in February 2005.[27] Once again I acted as a reviewer, and this time there were three other reviewers from overseas. The findings were essentially the same as those of the first report – that there was a statistically significant elevation in serum TCDD in the fifty-two Paritutū residents compared to national serum TCDD levels:

[H]istorical aerial emissions containing TCDD are responsible for the soil and serum dioxin concentrations in Paritutū. Observed chemical profiles of dioxin and its congeners in the Paritutū environment, its residents, and the measured TCDD elevations are most likely to be the result of fugitive emissions and not a result of combustion processes, such as incineration.[28]

Crucially, the report's authors were not able to identify which time periods had been most important, and one of the questions that remained unanswered, they concluded, was 'the temporal variation in exposures during the period 1962 to 1987'. From their viewpoint, and that of MoH, this was a relatively trivial question that the report had not been intended to answer. The survey was simply to find out if the long-term residents had received any significant TCDD exposure over and above the background level in the general population. They had, and the study had therefore achieved its main purpose.

Some community members attacked the report, however, particularly its conclusion that 'there was evidence of exposure to TCDD both pre- and post-1974, but no clearly demarcated exposure periods within the overall 25-year 2,4,5-T production period (i.e., 1962–1987) were evident'.[29] There was in fact some evidence in the report of more exposure before 1974 than after, but the numbers were too small to draw firm conclusions.

This was important to the community activists for two reasons. First, some of them believed that there had been massive exposures before the monitoring and restrictions introduced in 1974. Second, the period of peak exposure was crucial because it provided the date back to which the study findings should be extrapolated.

The half-life of TCDD in the body is about ten years. So if someone receives a massive exposure and gets high levels of TCDD in their blood, then ten years later the levels will only be half as large, and ten years after that they will be half as large again, and so on. The assumption of the authors of the ESR report was that exposure had stopped in 1987, when production ceased, and therefore that was the date back to which the data should be extrapolated. For example, the average level in the residents (10.8 parts per trillion (ppt)) was measured in 2004 – that is, seventeen years after exposure had apparently ceased. If we assume a half-life of ten years, then if the average level was 10.8 ppt in 2004, it would have been about twice as high ten years before (in 1994), and about three times as high seven years before that (1987). However, if the main exposures stopped in 1974, the data would have had to be extrapolated back another thirteen years, and the estimated peak exposure levels would have been about eight times higher in 1974 than the measured levels in 2004. This would mean the residents received exposures so high that they could not have occurred accidentally – supporting the activists' belief that there were negligently high levels of emissions pre-1974. MoH took the view that it didn't matter when the peak exposures happened – but it mattered to the activists.

This debate was complicated by some minor errors in the ESR reports. The first one mentioned a woman with high TCDD levels who had lived in the area for several years before 1974. In the second report, she seemed to have disappeared, or at least didn't appear in the right box in the presented tables. The implication was that correct classification would have strengthened the case for pre-1974 exposures being the most important.

The activists also started to ask why such apparent errors hadn't been picked up by the reviewers, and why the reviewers had not been given the 'raw data' (that is, the individual TCDD test results and the questionnaires for each study participant) to check.

I review many different types of documents, including reports and papers for scientific journals. I've done maybe one or two reviews a week for the last forty years – perhaps several thousand. I have never once been given the raw data to check. If asked to do this I would say no, because I simply wouldn't have the time. When you review a report, you assume that the numbers in the tables are correct, and that the data has been appropriately checked and re-checked by the authors. Instead, you focus on questions such as 'was the study design valid?' and 'are the conclusions valid, given the numbers presented in the tables?' It's very rare for the accuracy of the data itself to be questioned. If this does happen, an intensive independent audit of the data is required. What was unusual in this case was that the study had been published in two phases, and a careful comparison of the first and second reports would have shown at least one minor discrepancy between the tables.

The TV3 documentary

In September 2005 I organised a symposium in Wellington on 'Dioxin: Exposures, Health Effects and Public Policy'.[30] It included some of the top dioxin experts in the world, including Professor Pier Bertazzi from the University of Milan (who sadly died just as I was completing this book), Professor Kyle Steenland from Emory University in Atlanta, Georgia, and Professor Allan Smith from the University of California, Berkeley.[31] All three stressed that there was solid evidence TCDD could cause birth defects, cancer and some other diseases. However, all three also emphasised that the increased risks were fairly small, and that there was no reason to panic just because someone had an elevated TCDD level in their blood. The emphasis was on taking the risks seriously, but also on keeping them in perspective.

Various New Zealand-based researchers and representatives of the relevant government agencies also attended the symposium. The final session included 'community responses', particularly from organisations representing exposed workers, but also with contributions from community activists. This was unusual for an academic symposium, but I thought it important to have the activists there, and in fact they contributed a lot of local knowledge to the discussion.

Melanie Reid from TV3 had asked for, and received, permission to film the proceedings. She said she was making a documentary about the whole Paritutū story. Later, she contacted me by email asking if I had received the raw data from the survey when I reviewed the report. I said I hadn't, and wouldn't have expected to, and left it at that. I was surprised she didn't want to interview me about other issues – after all, I had been studying the workers at the factory for more than twenty years.

When the documentary appeared in 2006, none of the footage from the symposium had been used. The ninety-minute documentary didn't find space for even one minute showing the international experts who had spoken. Instead, there was picture after picture of babies born with birth defects, and interview after interview with people suffering from diseases such as cancer, which they believed had been caused by TCDD exposure. Some of them lived near the plant and probably had received some exposure. Others had never been near it and their exposure had been trivial – from spray drift when a farmer sprayed in a field near their house, for example. Even if the Paritutū exposures had been as high as the most extreme estimates, the number of extra cases of cancer or birth defects would be in single figures. This would be a tragedy, but it was highly unlikely that more than one or two of the people who appeared in the programme had suffered their diseases as a result of TCDD exposure. The others were almost certainly cases that would have occurred anyway. Completely ignored was the fact that about one in four people (25 per cent) get cancer some time in their life, and about 2–3 per cent of all births result in birth defects. If you go into any area in the country you will find plenty of cases of both.

The documentary also included an interview with a 'forensic accountant' who went through the ESR report and concluded that it had been inadequate and that there were mistakes in the data.[32] In one respect this was true. As noted earlier, there was a mistake with the classification of one study participant, but the effect of this was trivial unless you are assessing exposures before 1974. However, the documentary presented this as a major shortcoming of the report and made a big deal of the fact that the reviewers had not been sent the raw data. The programme included an 'ambush' interview with a spokesperson for MoH, which after all had not done the survey but had merely contracted ESR to do it. The flustered spokesperson was repeatedly asked why the reviewers had not been sent the raw data for checking.

The documentary was subject to a complaint by MoH to the Broadcasting Standards Authority, which concluded:

[291] ... the Authority has found that aspects of the broadcast of *Let Us Spray* breached standards of balance and fairness. The broadcaster failed to make reasonable efforts to include significant perspectives on the serum study and the health effects of dioxin, and this in turn led to ESR and MoH being treated unfairly.

[292] These matters were critical to the overall presentation of the controversial issue of public importance: whether public health authorities had adequately investigated, reported and acted on the beliefs of people who lived or worked in Paritutū that dioxin exposure had caused serious health effects (such as illness, deformity, and death) for them and their families.

[293] The Authority points out that its findings should not be viewed as restricting legitimate investigation and criticism of actions of government departments. It reiterates that this was an important story which deserved to be told; the people of Paritutū were entitled to express their beliefs about dioxin and how the

government had failed them. However, it is essential that investigations into controversial issues of public importance be presented in a fair and balanced way. This ensures that viewers are adequately informed of the issues, and that the people and organisations being criticised have a reasonable opportunity to put forward their side of the story.[33]

Following the screening, MoH announced that it would have the survey reviewed to check the claims about inaccuracies in the data. But it left it up to ESR to choose the reviewer. It was to be Allan Smith. (I must declare a conflict of interest here, as Allan was my PhD supervisor and remains a good friend.) Driving into work the next morning, I heard Sue Kedgley from the Green Party telling *Morning Report* that she had googled the name of Allan Smith and found that he had spoken at a meeting with myself (one of the ESR report reviewers) and Dr Don Matheson and Dr Mark Jacobs from MoH.[34] Clearly, therefore, he was not an independent person and should not be the report's reviewer.

She had found the website for the symposium, which of course included a wide range of people and a wide range of views – more or less the same wide range of people and views that I would have found if I had googled the name of Sue Kedgley and found that she regularly met in a place called 'Parliament'.

The next night, TV3 finally showed some of the film from our symposium – they had trawled through the recordings of the entire day and found five seconds of Allan Smith saying the ESR report was excellent. But he

was commenting not on whether the data was accurate –
like me, he hadn't seen the raw data – but on whether
the survey was well designed and clearly reported. It had
been, and it was appropriate for him to say so.

Because of the TV3-manufactured furore about Allan
Smith being the new reviewer, MoH hired two more
reviewers from overseas. All three cleared the ESR
report, saying that it was a good survey and that the minor
classification mistake had a trivial effect on the findings
and an even more trivial effect on their interpretation.
In the meantime, the 'storm in a cup of 2,4,5-T' about
the data had obscured the real issues. Whether you took
the original version of the data, or the slightly modified
corrected version, a scandal had occurred. The Paritutū
community had received TCDD exposure that should
never have happened, and almost certainly some of them
would have got cancer, or had babies with birth defects,
as a result.

What about the workers?

The main evidence about the effects of occupational
exposure to TCDD comes from the large international
IARC study, and four more detailed studies of highly
exposed groups of workers. I took part in the international collaborative study organised by the IARC,
which covered 21,863 workers in thirty-six cohorts
in twelve countries, including two New Zealand cohorts
(production workers and sprayers) that I contributed.[35]
In most cases the exposure occurred in the production
of phenoxy herbicides (the family of chemicals that

includes 2,4,5-T) and chlorophenols. A few groups suffered exposure through using these chemicals (such as by spraying 2,4,5-T).

However, the heaviest concentration of TCDD was probably experienced by production workers; TCDD is produced as a contaminant in the production process and then 'filtered out', so the product sprayed in the field usually contains much lower levels (with the exception of Agent Orange, where it was not so carefully filtered out). On the other hand, the sprayers could be assumed to have much greater exposure to the phenoxy herbicides themselves (for example, 2,4,5-T or 2,4-D). Thus, it is reasonable to conclude that production workers get the heaviest exposure to TCDD, whereas the sprayers get the heaviest exposure to the phenoxy herbicides themselves.

The 21,863 workers were followed for more than twenty years on average. By the end of follow-up, 4,026 of the male workers had died – slightly fewer than the number that would have been expected, based on national mortality rates in the countries where the study was done. This kind of result is quite common in occupational studies because of the 'healthy worker effect' – healthy people are more likely to get a job and to stay in employment, so employed people are almost always more healthy than the general population.[36]

We then did a more detailed analysis and found that the risk of cancer mortality in the TCDD-exposed group was 1.29 times that in the non-exposed group.[37] This 29 per cent increase is not large; active smoking, for instance, increases the risk of lung cancer by around 900 per cent (because smokers have about ten times the

49

risk of lung cancer compared with non-smokers). It is more similar to what you see with passive smoking and lung cancer, except that the increased risk from TCDD exposure applies to cancer in general, rather than just lung cancer. However, if you have an exposure that increases the risk of cancer in general, this can cause a lot of extra cases, even if the relative risk is low. Also, this relative risk estimate for cancer in general of 1.29 times is an average for all exposed workers in the factories included in the IARC cohort. The risks are substantially higher when we consider the most exposed workers, with relative risks closer to 2.0 (an increase of 100 per cent).[38]

As noted above, two New Zealand cohorts were part of the IARC study: one of 1,026 phenoxy herbicide production workers at what was then the IWD plant in New Plymouth, and one of 703 commercial sprayers of phenoxy herbicides.[39] IWD kindly granted me access as part of the study. Employment records were complete for the period from January 1969 to December 1984, covering workers who had worked at the plant for at least one month during that time. Also included were warehouse workers employed by the company in other parts of New Zealand, who frequently repacked or refilled containers. Excluded were kitchen, clerical and field research staff.

The cohort of sprayers included people listed at any time between January 1973 and December 1984 in the register of New Zealand chemical applicators. All were ground sprayers, mainly using backpack spraying and boom spraying from vehicles, and most were agricultural workers who sprayed mainly during summer months using 2,4,5-T and other phenoxy herbicides (as well as paraquat, organophosphate insecticides and other pesticides).

There was no increased risk of death from cancer, or of death in general, among the sprayers. For the 813 exposed production workers, however, the overall risk of death was almost exactly that expected based on national death rates – a relative risk (RR) of 0.99. This is unusual for most occupational cohorts, because of the healthy worker effect. The death rate from cancer was elevated, with 43 deaths compared to 34.6 expected based on national death rates. This difference was not statistically significant, but the relative risk of 1.24 in the exposed IWD workers was almost exactly the same as the relative risk of 1.29 for total cancer mortality in the overall IARC study. Although the numbers were small, the excess risks were greater in the departments that could be expected to have the greatest TCDD exposure: production workers (RR = 1.69), formulation and laboratory workers (1.64) and maintenance workers (1.46). The formulation and laboratory workers were the ones who actually made the 2,4,5-T by combining the ingredients, as well as carrying out research, so they probably had the highest exposures. Cancer deaths were not elevated in the other departments with lower TCDD exposure.

Although the findings for the IWD workers involved small numbers, they were consistent with the other larger international studies that had found increased cancer risks in TCDD-exposed workers. About 1 per cent of the workforce died from cancer because of their exposure, which is similar to the lifetime risk estimate by the US

Environmental Protection Agency (EPA US).[40] There was also concern that this figure might rise as the former workforce got older – if the relative risk of 1.24 continued into old age, when cancer is much more common, then the number of deaths from cancer due to TCDD exposure would keep rising proportionally.

The company

While all this was going on, Dow AgroSciences would call me from time to time. Whenever there was some news story about dioxin exposures in the Paritutū community, I would end up on television talking about the study we had done. I would stress that the workers probably had more exposure than the people living in the community, so the risks to the latter were probably lower than what I had seen. Eight or nine of the 813 exposed workers had died from cancer because of their TCDD exposure. About 800 people were living in the surrounding community at the time (some worked in the factory, but many didn't), so probably a few of them had also died from cancer because of their TCDD exposure. I didn't know how many (no one had done a study of the people in the community), but knew it must be fewer than eight or nine, and certainly much fewer than the dozens of deaths people had been claiming, because we would expect their exposures to be lower than those of the workers.[41]

The morning after I said this on the *Holmes* show in 2004, I got a call from the medical director for Dow in the Pacific area and the manager of the New Plymouth plant. They wanted to fund me to do further research, together with epidemiologists employed by Dow. I suggested instead that they give the funding to an independent body such as the HRC, which could make awards based on an open competitive process, but they didn't seem keen on this idea and, as I expected, I didn't hear back from them.

A few weeks later, however, I heard from a colleague, Alistair Woodward, at Wellington School of Medicine. Dow had asked him to work with them, but he knew that I was already studying these workers, so he called me to check. When I confirmed my involvement in the IARC study, Woodward told Dow he wasn't interested.

The renewed publicity about the New Plymouth plant got me thinking, and I decided it would be a good idea to update the follow-up and publish the New Zealand findings separately, which until now had been buried in the overall IARC study findings. I received the necessary funding from a Lotteries Health Research Grant.

Meanwhile, the approaches from Dow continued, both to me and Alistair Woodward. What Dow was suggesting was unusual in two respects. First, that epidemiologist based in the US would be leading the study, albeit while involving at least one New Zealand-based researcher. Second, the proposal was, in my opinion, essentially to duplicate the study I was already doing which involved workers employed before 1984, but to add on more recent workers, most of whom had not been exposed.

My study had covered everyone who worked at the plant between 1969 and 1984. The Dow study would include them all, plus people who had started work after 1984; but 2,4,5-T production had stopped in 1987, so almost all of the latter group would not have been exposed. In such an approach, data showing increased cancer risk in the exposed workers would be diluted by the findings from what turned out to be 500 new employees, who had not been exposed and would have low death rates because of the healthy worker effect (which is particularly strong for people who have started work recently). Woodward again turned down their proposal, and suggested they contact me.

They did, but no agreement was reached because of my insistence that Dow should not do the research itself but provide funding through an independent body such as the HRC. I should also stress that I am not inferring that there was anything suspect or biased about the proposed study – it was within the normal range of possible designs – but I had concerns about it, particularly because of the inclusion of more recent workers who were not exposed, and it was not the study that I would have chosen to do.

In 2004 the findings of our own study were presented in Melbourne at the International Meeting on Epidemiology in Occupational Health, which I co-hosted. A few days later I appeared on the *Holmes* show talking about what we had found. I had sent the company a copy of the paper a week or so before the Melbourne meeting. There was great interest in the findings because the study was appearing just a few months after the first Paritutū community survey results had been released, which raised concern about the general population's exposure to TCDD. I made the point again that the workers probably had more exposure than the residents. We had found an increased risk of cancer in the workers, and there could also be an increased risk, but a much lower one, in the residents.

The new study

Following the release of the first findings of the community serum dioxin study in 2004, and my media appearances asking why nothing was being done for the workers, we started to get calls from workers who were concerned about their health.[42] They wanted medical checks, or blood tests for TCDD. There was nothing much we could do for them (we didn't have any funding), but we started to keep a file of who had called and promised to keep them informed. Eventually we decided to do a new study, selecting a random sample of the workers who we knew were still alive on 31 December 2000, giving them a clinical examination by a doctor and testing their blood for TCDD. The HRC gave us the necessary funding ($1.1 million) in May 2005 and we got ethical approval from the Massey University Human Ethics Committee (MUHEC), which was forwarded to the HRC – it's necessary to do this before the grant can be activated.

In the meantime, in early 2005 I began to hear rumours that Dow had launched their own study with a New Zealand researcher – an occupational health specialist at another university – as co-investigator. I knew the person concerned and was surprised that he had apparently accepted the funding without first checking with me. Just over a year later, on 13 March 2006, the authors of the Dow study issued a press statement entitled 'Otago Study Provides Assurance for Former 2,4,5-T Workers'.[43] This was highly unusual, issuing a press statement about the findings of a study yet to be peer reviewed and published in a journal, and for which no manuscript was available that would enable others to review the findings. Given the inclusion of hundreds of non-exposed workers in the study, it was not surprising that the authors wound up providing 'assurance'.

Ethics

Our HRC grant took effect from 1 July 2005, though the money did not come through straight away. With most of these grants, the HRC takes a couple of months to process the paperwork, but you get started anyway, as we did in August – though we had not written to any potential participants yet. As far as we knew, the funding was about to start coming, backdated to the study's start date.

Before I say what happened next, perhaps I should give a brief description of how the New Zealand system of ethical review works.

Each university has its own ethics committee, which reviews and gives ethical approval to any research on humans being done within the university. Most agencies that fund research won't release the money to the university until such approval is given. The HRC requires this approval to come from an HRC-accredited committee – as the MUHEC is – that has met certain criteria about its membership and processes.

There is also a system of regional health ethics committees, now called health and disability ethics committees, set up specifically to deal with health research, particularly if it involves patients or patient records. They are administered by MoH, but the HRC also accredits them and is much more closely involved with them than with the university-based ones. HRC regulations require researchers to apply to their institutional (university) ethics committee unless there is a reason why the study should be referred to a regional health ethics committee. Reasons include any research study involving the collection of human tissues where the research study is to be reviewed by an Institutional Ethics Committee which does not have a health professional present at the discussion who is qualified to assess the safety of the procedures. Our IWD study did involve collecting blood samples, but the MUHEC included a medical doctor qualified to assess the safety of the procedures. We had applied to that committee – which was the correct one to go to – and received approval.

Sitting at my desk one morning, I got a phone call from a colleague who was a member of the Central Ethics Committee (CEC), the one covering the lower half of the North Island. It was quite a new committee because the national system of ethical review had been revised – in fact, I had been part of the National Ethics Advisory Committee (I was nominated to it by the HRC) that did the revising. The new system of six committees throughout the country had only started in 2005.[44]

My colleague told me the CEC had received an application for the Dow study. It had had a number of concerns about it, particularly the heavy involvement of the company in the study, but most of these concerns had been worked out to its satisfaction. However, the Dow researchers had now come back with a new request, namely, to collect blood samples from some of the workers. My colleague was concerned that two different research groups might wind up approaching the same workers for samples. I confirmed that we were already doing a study and would send out the first invitations to participants in the following month or so. I also emailed all our documentation to let the CEC know what we were doing and offered to come along to a committee meeting if its members wanted to know anything more.

I expected to hear from the committee, but instead on 5 September the university received an HRC email requesting copies of our ethics applications to the MUHEC.

Interestingly, the HRC had not raised this issue with another study (of timber workers, discussed in the next chapter) that also involved blood samples, which it had already funded after accepting ethical approval from the MUHEC. The only explanation for there being a problem this time around appeared to be that the CEC had complained to the HRC about the MUHEC approving a study that the CEC felt should have come to it. We were becoming trapped in a turf war between two ethics committees. I never quite worked out why the HRC was so clearly siding with the CEC, though it is true that although the HRC was accrediting both the regional ethics committees (like the CEC) and the university-based ones (like the MUHEC) it seemed to have much stronger links with the regional committees.

That battle dragged on until May 2005, during which time the HRC repeatedly threatened not to start the funding unless we gave it copies of our MUHEC ethical approvals. Massey took the attitude, correctly in my view, that the MUHEC had been officially accredited by the HRC, and it was inappropriate for the latter to be interfering in the former's decisions – the HRC was supposed to accredit the committee and then be 'hands off'. It was a stalemate, made worse when Dow wrote to the HRC complaining that its own study had been held up, various cabinet ministers got involved, and the whole thing nearly ended up in court.

Dow eventually backed off, and we agreed that our two studies would coexist and we would cooperate so that workers were not asked to give two blood samples. I wasn't completely happy with this, as I didn't want to be associated with the Dow study, but I would have to be if we wanted our study to go ahead as well. So we agreed to stay independent but to keep each other informed, and to cooperate where necessary and possible.

So that was sorted out, but we still had the problem with the HRC. This was particularly ironic because the whole mess had arisen from my refusing to take funding directly from Dow and advocating the more ethical route of working through the HRC – which, along with the CEC, didn't appear concerned about the ethics of what the company was doing. They also didn't seem to see the ethical contradiction in their attacking our study, which was independent, university-based, supported by WHO and funded by the HRC, whereas in my opinion, the Dow study did not meet all of these criteria. All they appeared concerned about was a stupid turf war between ethics committees.

It went on for months, with the HRC refusing to sign the contract, withholding the funding, and continuing to demand copies of our ethics applications under the Official Information Act. We didn't want to hand over the applications because it would set a bad precedent of permitting the HRC to interfere in the work of one of its accredited committees.

In November 2005 I decided that the only way out of it, without going to court, was to meet with the CEC and tell them the full story. I did this in December. The CEC then invited us to make a completely new application to it, which we did, eventually receiving ethical approval in May 2006. The process took longer than usual, partly because the CEC was trying to treat our study and Dow's equally (the irony of this doesn't seem to have occurred to it) and to approve them at the same time.

Finally, when the new ethical approval came through, I sent the documentation to the HRC and asked that the funding be backdated a few months to reflect the work already done on the project – we hadn't seen any participants yet, but we had done a huge amount in terms of gaining the ethical approval(s), preparing questionnaires, databases and mailing lists, and responding to HRC correspondence. This sort of backdating of a grant is quite standard. However, Massey received a response from the HRC asking why the research had already started: 'What has been done and why was the research commenced, prior to receiving ethical approval, and a signed contract from the HRC? Did Massey University give Professor

Pearce permission to commence the research?' The HRC also continued to demand copies of the previous ethics applications before signing the contract. My interpretation was that the HRC had got it wrong in the first place by saying the MUHEC did not have the authority to approve the study, when it clearly did. It had then painted itself into a corner by demanding copies of the ethics applications. The issue had nearly ended up in court, and all the government agencies and ministers that had got involved commented to me, at least in private, that the HRC was in the wrong but that they couldn't interfere. By now we had the new CEC ethical approval, and we had all the other boxes ticked, some more than once. So we gave the HRC the MUHEC applications and approvals, and never heard a word about them – there was never anything wrong with them.

Both studies finally went ahead, and we cooperated to the extent necessary. It went reasonably smoothly, albeit with some misunderstandings caused by the fact that we were sometimes studying and consulting with the same people, including local iwi, since the workforce included a high proportion of Māori workers. I had one particularly confusing phone call with a kaumatua (Māori community leader) from New Plymouth, who criticised me angrily for something I had done, or not done. It went on for some time before I realised that he had the wrong guy, but by then it was too late to persuade him – I eventually found someone else to consult with. I should stress that I strongly support the need for Māori community consultation – I helped push for it and make it a requirement when I chaired the HRC Public Health Committee, and I was a member of the HRC Māori Health Committee and later on the HRC Pacific Health Committee. It's just that sometimes such consultation works well, and sometimes it doesn't (particularly because of the lack of resources and funding for local iwi), and this isn't helped when you have confusion because of two similar studies being done at the same time.

What our new study found

We surveyed 245 former employees of the Dow factory, all of whom had been employed at some time between 1969 and 1984.[45] They were interviewed in person, we took a blood sample, and a subgroup had a neurological examination. It was an incredibly difficult study to do. The fieldwork often involved a team travelling around with a research fellow conducting the interviews, a research nurse to draw blood, and an occupational physician doing the neuropsychological testing. For some blood tests the lymphocytes had to be cultured within four hours of the sample being taken. About half the participants still lived in the New Plymouth area, but the other half were scattered around the country. To test a couple of people in Invercargill, for example, involved booking a clinic, the nurse flying down there, obtaining the samples and then flying back and getting them to the laboratory assistant within four hours. A lot could go wrong, and sometimes it did, but we got there in the end, more or less.

What did we find? The sixty men who had worked in the phenoxy/TCP production area had a mean TCDD serum concentration of 19.1 pg/g lipid, three times the levels of the 141 men and 43 women employed in other parts of the plant (6.3 and 6.0 pg/g, respectively), and about double what had been observed in ESR's survey of residents. Diabetes was four times as common in those who had worked in TCDD-exposed jobs, as were non-fasting glucose levels (a marker of diabetes). The TCDD-exposed workers also had higher risks of a range of subclinical responses in multiple systems (peripheral nervous system, immune system, thyroid hormones and lipid metabolism). This was all several decades after their last exposure – production stopped in 1987, but some of the participants had left the company before then, and we did the survey about twenty years later.

We also asked about their children – 127 men and twenty-one women reported that 355 children were conceived after they started work at the plant. The proportion of male babies was 55 per cent, which is a bit higher than what you see in the general population, where it's more like 51 per cent. However, in those whose fathers had had high TCDD exposure, the proportion of male babies was only 47 per cent, and the ratio decreased with increasing paternal exposure. This trend has been seen in some other populations with high TCDD exposure (such as in the Italian town of Seveso, which had major exposure after an industrial accident). The same thing has been observed with some other environmental toxins.[46]

The reasons for this reduced sex ratio are not clear, and of course it is not a bad thing in itself to have a few more girl babies than expected. However, it seems to be the canary in the mine of environmental reproductive health. If a chemical is altering the sex ratio, it is likely to be having other reproductive effects as well, such as occasional congenital malformations; but this was an outcome we didn't have large enough numbers to assess.[47]

4. Trouble at Mill

It had started like a normal day at work. I checked my email, went for a coffee and a muffin, returned to the office and started some real work. Then the phone rang. It was some assistant to the Associate Minister of Health. Did I know that a community meeting in Whakatāne yesterday evening had voted unanimously that my study of former timber workers should be stopped, and that the money should be given to the workers to test their dioxin levels? I didn't. And did I know that the minister now also wanted the study stopped? I didn't know that either. So how did it get to this?

2,4,5-T was the only commonly used agricultural chemical contaminated with TCDD. Plenty of others, however, were contaminated with other types of dioxin. The most common of these was PCP, which was introduced as a wood preservative by Dow and Monsanto in 1936. It was widely used for timber treatment in New Zealand from 1936 until 1988, when the timber industry voluntarily withdrew it from use because of concerns about its effects on the environment (not its effects on the workers). At that time, New Zealand was the last Western country still widely using PCP, which by 1989 was banned in ten countries: Sweden, Denmark, Greece, Egypt, Italy, Liechtenstein, Nicaragua, Panama, Switzerland and West Germany. In 1991 the Pesticides

Board finally deregistered it and made it a prohibited import. In 2016 the IARC classified it as a confirmed human carcinogen.[1]

PCP was used as a fungicide to prevent the growth of sapstain fungi.[2] New Zealand was a particularly heavy user because the timber industry is (proportionally) a major part of the economy, and more than 90 per cent of the timber produced is *Pinus radiata*, which is, along with other softwoods, more susceptible to sapstain. Mixed with oil, PCP was infused by high steam pressure into the timber; or, diluted with water, sprayed or brushed on.[3]

PCP was never manufactured in New Zealand: it was imported from Brazil, China, Mexico, India, France and the US.

The main route of PCP exposure is through the skin, with about 50 per cent or more of oil-based formulations being absorbed that way.[4] Absorption can also occur through inhalation and ingestion. Once absorbed, about 86 per cent is excreted within a week. There have been varying estimates of the half-life in blood and/or urine, ranging from 30 hours to 72 days.[5] However, this is the half-life for PCP itself; the dioxin contaminants are believed to have much longer half-lives, similar to that for TCDD, which is about ten years.

I recall visiting a sawmill in the 1980s and seeing the pools of chemicals lying around everywhere. Only some timber needs anti-sapstain treatment, but it was usually easiest to treat all the timber routinely. It would be cut up and dipped in baths of PCP before being sorted. The highest exposures would be in the workers mixing the PCP and sorting the treated timber. Dave McLean (who worked for the Engineers Union, in the timber industry, and later for my research group) comments:[6]

> I have seen timber treated with ... sapstain control fungicides being pulled off the sorting table. The workers lift heavy pieces of timber and lever them on their hips, saturating their clothing with the solution. The saturated clothing is worn all day and as the main route of exposure is through dermal contact, there is a very strong potential for uptake.[7]

The working conditions were also described by some former timber workers at the symposium on dioxin (see Chapter 3) that we held in September 2005:

> The table hands worked on the green table day in, day out. The green table was based on a dirt floor. Treated timber used to come along the table and the workers would pull it off in racks. They would then stack the timber and consequently would become drenched in the PCP. Maintenance workers became drenched in it as well when they worked on the table's mechanical systems.
>
> The only time that protection was worn was in the winter, but it was worn to protect the workers from the cold. At times they wore aprons, but the aprons only created a reservoir for the liquid to go down into their boots. People would cut holes in their gumboots to prevent them from filling up with the liquid. It was always easy to spot a new table hand, because his gumboots were overflowing with PCP. Workers were supplied with gloves, but when the temperature dropped

to three degrees below zero, the gloves became brittle. They would break and become useless ...

The smoko room was right next door to the dip plant so workers had to walk through the dip plant to get to the smoko room. The closest building to the dip plant was the Kinleith cafeteria where over 2,000 workers used to partake daily in their meals. Prevailing winds through all the contaminated dust used to come through the dip plant and over to the cafeteria.[8]

After New Zealand stopped using PCP, a study of sediment cores in Manukau Harbour found unexpectedly high levels of chlorine-based chemicals, including PCP.[9] The Cawthron Institute in Nelson was then commissioned by the Ministry for the Environment to do a study of the use of PCP and chlordane. In its report, published in 1990, the institute found that in the 1980s New Zealand used up to 200 tonnes of PCP a year, mainly in the timber industry, but also to control slime in pulp and paper production. About 5,000 tonnes were used in total.[10] The report concluded that there were possibly 800 contaminated sites – mostly current or former timber mills – and the whereabouts of about half of these were unknown.

The ministry set up a national task group (NTG), including representatives from the industry, DSIR, MoH, iwi and the Timber Workers Union. The group's first report identified the Waipā mill site as being of particular concern with regard to PCP but also for dioxin and other related contaminants (polychlorinated dibenzodioxins (PCDDs) and dibenzofurans (PCDFs)):

The Waipa sawmill, established in 1939, is about five
kilometres south of Rotorua ... The mill has been
progressively modified and expanded over the last
53 years and is currently the largest stand-alone sawmill
in the country ... Significant concentrations of PCP
and PCDDs/PCDFs ... were found in soils adjacent to
areas where PCP was used during wood processing
and where waste disposal had taken place ... PCP
contamination was found at both surface and depth
and the results suggested that vertical migration
occurred within the soil profile, potentially resulting
in contamination of groundwater. PCP contaminated
groundwater is migrating toward the Waipa Stream,
and the site stormwater drainage system may be acting
as a collection system ... The study results indicate that
the contamination of the groundwater by PCP is likely
to be adversely affecting the aquatic ecosystems of the
Waipa stream. PCP and PCDDs/PCDFs were detected
in fish, mussels and sediments in Lake Rotorua. There
is no clear indication of significant adverse effects in
the aquatic ecosystems of Lake Rotorua, or that the
contamination observed poses a concern with regard to
human health.[11]

One sample taken at the Waipā mill had the highest dioxin
levels ever recorded in a soil sample.[12]

The NTG report was not well received by the industry,
even though the industry was represented in the group.
An OSH scientist, who was also a member of the
group, was reported as saying:

It is far from clear whether the industry has [a] commitment to the objectives of the NTG. After hearing a figure of $3 million described as probably inadequate to clean up the Waipa site ... it would be understandable if industry became circumspect of the NTG goals. It is possible that many companies would be bankrupted by this level of expenditure, leaving New Zealand under-represented in a key export industry and the state lumbered with the full responsibility for site remediation.[13]

Nationally, the estimated costs of cleaning up the sites ranged from a timber industry estimate of $20 million to one of $175 million.[14] Although, under the Resource Management Act, the costs must be covered by the site owners, this is complicated because the sites have changed hands many times.[15]

The environmental contamination was of particular concern for local Māori, many of whose ancestors have lived on the land for hundreds of years:

The local Māori people, the tangata whenua, are the people of the land, and do not consider themselves in isolation from it. Iwi Māori have been at particular risk from further contamination as they continue their customary practices of gathering food such as eels from the rivers and shellfish from the river mouths ... Some of the small creeks and rivers adjacent to the mills are no longer capable of sustaining life, removing the formerly available food sources, whilst the gathering and consumption of shellfish elsewhere is a continuing concern ...

Whilst the poisoning of the trout has been studied, eels and the filter feeding shellfish have not attracted the same attention in the media, the implication of which is that preferential concern is given to the sports fishermen and New Zealand's 'clean' image overseas, whilst sidelining the indigenous population.[16]

It was only in the 1980s that media stories started to appear about the dangers of PCP exposure. After all, it didn't contain TCDD, which was what most people meant when they used the word 'dioxin'. For example, the Waipā mill manual stated that 'with proper precautions it may be used with absolute safety'.[17]

However, there has always been concern about the health effects of PCP exposure.[18] The acute symptoms include irritation of the skin, eyes and airways, chloracne, fever, sweating, nausea, vomiting, loss of appetite, dizziness and loss of balance, increased heart rate and reduced urinary output.[19] Although the acute effects depend on the exposure experienced in the previous few days, the chronic health effects more often depend on the long-term cumulative exposure, and may occur many years after exposure has ceased.

With regards to chronic health effects, various government agencies took the approach that 'if we don't see them then they don't exist'. For example, a Health Department scientist, Chris Shaw, was quoted as saying:

Timber workers you would see as being the most highly exposed group and according to the Department of Labour, they have not been able to see any significant

71

adverse effects from the use of PCP. Now, if in the highly exposed group you can't see an effect, you are going to be even less likely to see an effect in a group that could be minimally exposed.[20]

Of course, DoL and other government agencies had no idea whether timber workers really had health problems, because no one had studied them. Instead, they relied on individual doctors to make a notification that one of their patients had developed a disease because of exposure to PCP. In fact, many GPs don't know what jobs their patients do, or don't think it matters – a GP is very unlikely to make a connection between an occupational exposure and a disease in one of their patients if they have not first been informed by DoL that this is a possibility:

> They would take sick leave for dermatitis and skin
> diseases, go to the doctor and get some cream – instead
> of it being recognised and diagnosed as occupational
> dermatitis. Therefore ACC don't have records of past
> skin diseases and neither does the Health Department,
> even though there is a requirement under law that they
> must be notified.[21]

Thus, the reports that workers were making through their unions and community organisations were quite different from those appearing in official statistics. Red Middlemiss, from the Engineering, Printing and Manufacturing Union (EPMU), reported:

When the Kinleith sawmill shut down in the early eighties, a lot of the employees transferred elsewhere in New Zealand Forest Products. Some years later I went through a list of the workers who had worked on the green table. My aim was to ascertain residual effects from the chemicals. I asked a colleague from the mill to assist me in contacting as many of these people as possible. We managed to establish a database of 40 names and started to make contact with the people listed ...

- Of the 40 people who used to work on the green chain that we made contact with, 10 were deceased. Only two of the deceased were aged over 50 ...
- Of the remaining 29 people, two would not commit to writing anything for the interviews.
- Eleven of the remaining 27 were very ill.

Most of the sick people had been experiencing bad headaches and night sweats, insomnia and aching joints. Five had developed cancer. Two of these cases were bowel cancer. One man had very bad dermatitis that actually smelled as you approached him. Four people had other serious skin complaints from dermatitis to boils and welts, and one person had welts all around his neck and on his face.[22] Middlemiss also told the story of a mate who had died while he was doing his research:

I spoke with a friend that used to run the dip plant, his name was Jackie Joseph. Jackie reported to me that he had actually fallen right into the tank and nearly drowned. Since that day, he had suffered from headaches, night sweats and other various ailments including rashes ...

Before I could interview Jackie again, he developed a tumour in his head, and he could not lean forward as this would bring on a mini-stroke. He used to have to sleep upright, sitting in a chair. About 8 months later, Jackie was dead, in his mid forties. He was a mate of mine. I have got no answers for his family. They think he died because he fell in the dip tank. His workmates also think that his death has something to do with that.[23]

In about 1996, various worker organisations started to take action on the health effects of PCP. The initial work was done by the Wood Industries Union of Aotearoa and was later taken up by EPMU, which created a register of PCP-exposed workers.

Sawmill Workers Against Poisons (SWAP) was established as an action group in 1996. It was led by Joe Harawira, whom I eventually got to know and regarded with great admiration. Sadly, Joe died in 2017, after spending the last thirty years of his life campaigning about PCP, and dioxin more generally. SWAP campaigned not only for recognition for workers at the Whakatāne sawmill harmed by workplace chemical poisoning, but also to have all remaining contaminated sites cleaned up, including twenty-five dumps in the Whakatāne area. For many decades the mill had dumped contaminated sawdust, bark, scrap timber and chemicals in and around the town. One story that Joe told me involved a site where they had campaigned to have the PCP-contaminated soil dug up and moved. According to Joe, the company eventually did this, but it also pulled down the nearby mill, which was full of asbestos, and got rid of the asbestos by putting it in the new hole they had dug. Clearly, the company had much to learn about the sanctity of the land, particularly for Māori.

A group of medical students who did a project on PCP workers in 1999 described attending a meeting of the workers:

> Having listened to the men and their wives who talked with clear sincerity, there was no doubt that the mill workers who had been exposed to PCP had suffered debilitating illnesses, both acute and chronic, and were feeling frustrated at having their stories fall on deaf ears ...
>
> Following dinner we attended a public meeting organised by the Ministry for the Environment. At this meeting medical and scientific experts presented summaries of their studies ... I found their presentations difficult to follow despite several years of attending [university] ... The responses from the floor did not relate to the presentations, but rather reflected real concerns for the local community. It was a classic case of talking past each other as the speakers failed to under-stand where the community speakers were coming from, and instead made efforts to interpret their concerns into their scientific parameters, thereby missing the message altogether.[24]

Shortly after the creation of SWAP, Ninox Films produced a television documentary about PCP, which included the testing of blood samples from four workers.

75

This showed that three of them had high serum levels of dioxin, particularly the two types of dioxin that are common contaminants of PCP.

A subsequent report prepared for the Ministry for the Environment in 2001 concluded:

> Based on a small number of blood samples and measurements of PCDDs, the New Zealand sawmill workers appear to be a unique group in that their exposure manifest now in their blood analyses was to hexa- and hepta-PCDDs, and not to 2,3,7,8-TCDD ... Such exposures may occur elsewhere in the world with PCP contaminants, but we are not aware of any documentation of this ... While it is not possible to draw conclusions about health effects from the small number of workers assessed so far, it is clear that human studies are needed of workers with these exposures.
>
> With regard to those workers already known to be exposed, it should be noted that they have concentrations of toxic chemicals in their blood much increased beyond those in the general New Zealand population. Whether or not they would experience symptoms and health effects at these concentrations is not known. However, in contrast to often unwarranted fears of chemical exposure, these workers have biologically proven concentrations of PCDD/Fs in their bodies. Furthermore, there is no known treatment to remove these contaminants from them ... because these chemicals have long half-lives, these workers continue to be exposed for many years after their workplace exposure ceased.[25]

As a result of this report, the following year OSH – which was part of DoL – commissioned my research group to investigate the feasibility of studying the health effects of PCP exposure in former timber workers. Our preliminary proposal had two main parts: (i) an historical cohort study of deaths and cancer incidence; or (ii) a cross-sectional morbidity study in a random sample of people who had worked in the timber industry at the time PCP was used. It was noted that both studies would require access to historical records of employment and exposure.

You might ask why we needed to do a study when there had been so many reports of health problems, and registers of timber workers with illnesses had already been assembled by the unions and SWAP. The problem with such registers is that they are based on volunteers and involve quite a small proportion of the 20,000 or so people who have worked in the industry. If you have a voluntary register with just a few hundred people, and 30 per cent of them have diabetes, what can you conclude from this information? Do former timber workers really have a higher than usual rate of diabetes? Or are they just more likely to volunteer to join a register if they have a health problem like diabetes? The most you can say is that the information from such registers can show there *may* be a problem that should be checked out in a proper study. The authorities tend to dismiss the evidence from voluntary registers ('it doesn't prove anything') and revert to their default position that 'there is no problem'. The workers, however, tend to take the mirror-image approach and assume that 'where there's smoke, there's fire'.

Studies of PCP

I helped with a survey of former timber workers published in 1998.[26] Using the information from a questionnaire completed by 127 of them, we attempted to classify them into low, medium and high categories of lifetime exposure to PCP. A significant dose-response was found between past exposure and reported symptoms of fever/sweating (47 per cent in the high group compared with 29 per cent in the low), weight loss (33 and 16 per cent, respectively), persistent fatigue (74, 53), nausea (40, 16) and responses to a screening test for neuropsychological dysfunction (81, 62). Associations were also observed with emphysema and chronic bronchitis. At the time, I was told that the findings were not well received by activists concerned about PCP, who believed workers were suffering many other health conditions (for example, diabetes) – but SWAP did eventually cite the study on its website as evidence of a problem.

Nearly ten years later, when the issue of PCP was in the news again, we tried to set up a better and more comprehensive study. The only way of finding out whether there really are more health problems in former timber workers is to study all the workers in one or more mills, or at least all who worked there during a particular period. This involves going to a mill, talking with the management, and asking to see the personnel records to determine their suitability for a study.

We then did a feasibility study and found, to our surprise, that sufficient records were available from five sawmills, and that exposure information was available from two New Zealand surveys of PCP uptake in 155 sawmill workers in the late 1980s. This was enough to do a good study.

Problems with ethics

No sooner had we received funding for the study than problems began. The first one involved the ethical approval. It might seem strange to the average reader that we are allowed to get access to personnel records for a study like this. Actually, it's quite straightforward, provided you have ethical approval, keep everything confidential, and remove the names from the main data file once you have linked everything up so that the data is no longer identifiable. I and others have gotten approval for many studies like this previously.

However, some ethics committee members don't understand the Privacy Act, and usually have had no training on it. So their first reaction is usually 'you can't do that, because of the Privacy Act'. This is what happened when we applied to the MUHEC in December 2003. It took four months, and the commissioning of an independent legal opinion to show that the committee was wrong, before we finally obtained ethical approval in April 2004.

During those four months we couldn't do any work on the project and, as a result, other problems developed. When we first discussed the study with OSH, my main concern had been that DoL and MoH might use the study as an excuse for not doing anything until it was finished – which would take a couple of years. Groups such as SWAP clearly had many members with serious health problems they believed were caused by PCP. We didn't know whether this was true or not, but in any case, people were sick and needed help. The study shouldn't be an excuse to do nothing. However, it looked like this was exactly what was happening. I still hadn't managed to meet SWAP because I was held up by the problems with ethical approval. SWAP had written to the Associate Minister of Health, Damien O'Connor, in December 2003, and he replied on 5 February 2004:

> I am concerned that you continue to feel that the health issues of sawmill workers are not being adequately addressed ... With regards to health matters, the principal focus now is the epidemiological studies that are to be undertaken by the Centre for Public Health Research, Massey University, and which are funded by Occupational Safety and Health, Department of Labour ... Planning for the epidemiological studies commences this month ... It is anticipated that both studies will be completed in approximately two years.

So the study was being used as an excuse to do nothing to help the community for two years. Moreover, the minister never told me he'd sent this letter – I only found out about it from SWAP. Naturally, they were not happy – I wouldn't have been either if I were them – and they took out their frustration on O'Connor when he came to Whakatāne for a public meeting on 14 April 2004.

By all accounts it was a masterful performance. The meeting started with the reading of the apologies – including the names of all the former timber workers who had died. In his unpublished notes on the meeting, Dr Phil Shoemack (Medical Officer of Health for Bay of Plenty) wrote:

> SWAP presented the recent history of their group and a précis of actions taken since the hui at Pupuaruhe Marae in December 2001. They explained that the identification and investigation of contaminated sites around Whakatane township was progressing well ... They emphasized that they have ongoing concerns about the poor health status of SWAP members and their families, which they are convinced is a direct result of historic and ongoing exposure to timber treatment chemicals.

When O'Connor responded by saying that the issue of health effects was being addressed by our study, the meeting, quite naturally, erupted with anger. As Shoemack summarised it, SWAP's demands at the end of the meeting were that the minister should:

- Stop the OSH-funded research being conducted by Prof Neil Pearce. They say the research is flawed and it is not necessary anyway as SWAP already knows what is causing their health problems.
- Free access for SWAP members and their families to a special clinic to be set up specifically for treating people exposed to timber treatment chemicals. The clinic must offer on-demand and free dioxin testing to measure the 'body burden' of dioxin, genetic testing and diagnosis and

treatment of all other conditions. The clinic will probably need to be mobile and must be able to refer on to whatever secondary or tertiary services are required.

- People seen at the clinic will be entered into a database of timber treatment chemical exposed people so that research can be conducted to confirm the health consequences of their exposure.

I didn't know about any of this until the next day, when a person from O'Connor's office called me demanding the study be stopped. It seemed that the minister was acceding to SWAP's demands. I explained that: (i) if he wanted to offer dioxin testing for SWAP members, he should offer it to all former timber workers – there were 20,000 of them, and it cost $1,200 a time, so the cost would be $24 million, not the $0.5 million that we had available for the study; (ii) Massey had signed a contract to do the study, and it couldn't be broken just because the minister wanted the money for something else; (iii) he was Associate Minister of Health and the study was being funded by DoL, so it was none of his business. I hung up and didn't respond to the dozen or so messages I received over the following three days. I refused to meet unless the Minister of Labour, Ruth Dyson, was also there – after all, her department was funding the study – and in the end I only met with Dyson, and the pressure from O'Connor faded away.

I decided to note the impact of recent activities on the study by sending a general letter to all concerned. It was addressed to DoL's chief executive, James Buwalda, but copied to all the relevant officials, ministers, the HRC, the Massey administration, unions and community groups, including SWAP:

When we first applied to do this study, I expressed concern both to Bob Hill [DoL's chief health and safety advisor] and to the then Minister of Labour (Hon Margaret Wilson) that the study needed to be seen as part of a larger package of support for the communities of former timber workers (I should stress that these are spread throughout New Zealand, not just in the Bay of Plenty). Such a package of support would involve both the Ministry of Health and OSH getting involved in providing advice and support, help with access to health services, advice on applying for compensation from ACC, etc, to all of the former workforce (not just those involved in particular lobby groups such as SWAP). I was assured by Bob Hill that this would occur, and indeed the RFP [OSH's request for proposal] stated that it would occur.

The project has got off to a rocky start. It is supported by the two key unions who cover the former workforce in this industry (the Northern Distribution Union and the Engineering, Printing and Manufacturing Union), but there is apparently some concern about the study amongst members of SWAP. This doesn't mean that the study shouldn't go ahead. However, I think that their concerns are justified in that OSH does not appear to have done what it promised to do in the RFP. If the workforce is not being provided with advice and support, as promised in the RFP, and if the study is the only thing that is happening, it is quite reasonable for former timber workers to be sceptical about the study and to see it as being used as an excuse for not providing help with their health concerns which are immediate and real ...

In this respect, I would note that the Ministry of Health has already done quite a lot to provide support and advice to former timber workers ... It is important that OSH gets involved in the issue at a similar level and at least to the same extent ... If such involvement from OSH doesn't occur, and if the study is the only thing that is happening, then it is going to be very difficult to do the study and I wouldn't blame the workforce for being sceptical about it.

Two days later Gwenda Paul from SWAP called me saying that at last they understood where the hold-ups had been. We were both on the same side, and we agreed to meet as soon as possible. SWAP then wrote to O'Connor on 15 May saying that it seemed people had been talking at cross purposes but that all the issues were now being resolved:

As a result of these issues being clarified we firstly wish to withdraw our demand to have the Neil Pearce research project withdrawn and in fact NOW wish to support it with the following conditions:

1. That SWAP officials be a mandatory part of the participative research, the advisory body and any other committee that may be set up as part of the Research Funding Project (RFP).

2. That the research in no way inhibits the development of the immediate health care project as outlined to you by SWAP at our meeting.

3. Part of the health project will be a database set up to monitor the health of ex-sawmill workers AND THEIR FAMILIES.

Problems with the company

In the meantime, things had also not gone well with the company that owned the five mills. Between submitting the feasibility study report and starting the main study, they had sold one mill and destroyed its personnel records, and were refusing access to the other four mills. Following a meeting, it again agreed to give access but under conditions that we considered draconian and unacceptable – for example, that the company could reclaim the information and destroy it at any time.

We eventually obtained access to the records from three of the mills, but this involved negotiations lasting from July 2004 (when the study was supposed to start) until November 2005, when we finally got the last of the records we needed. During this time we also obtained records from other mills held in the national archives (many former sawmills had been state-owned, so their personnel records were government property). These records were held in Auckland, but we were denied permission to take them to Wellington for a few days for copying and had to pay to have archives staff copy them.

While these negotiations with the company were going on, we discussed things with OSH and agreed that I would write to OSH formally asking for help with obtaining copies of the personnel records, and that I should copy the correspondence to the HRC (which was administering the OSH funding) to keep it informed.

To my surprise, Massey then received a call from HRC's chief executive, complaining about my dragging him into the negotiations. This was the first of many problems with the HRC, which ran in parallel with the issues we had been having with the IWD study (see Chapter 3).

The problems came to a head in August 2005 when I was at a meeting of the International Epidemiological Association in Bangkok. I had just (one hour before) been elected president of the association, and I made the mistake of checking my emails before the conference dinner. When I saw one headed 'problem with PCP study', I knew I didn't want to deal with it that evening so just filed it to look at when I got home. Back in Wellington, I got a call from the Massey administration saying they had been informed that the HRC had unilaterally suspended the funding for the study. One day later the HRC also halted the funding (which had not yet started) for the IWD study. Suddenly we were $1.6 million poorer. I asked the HRC for clarification, particularly since we were hosting a major meeting on dioxin the next day (see Chapter 3) and planned to talk about the study. The HRC told us we couldn't even mention the study at the symposium. We did anyway – we had people from all over the world attending, as well as members of SWAP, and we couldn't just sit there and say nothing. Eventually, after a three-month delay, the study went ahead.

What the study found

One big problem was that none of the sawmills for which we had access were the mills where most of the main SWAP members had worked. When I went with two of my staff (who were both Māori health researchers) to meet the SWAP members, I had to stand up before a large group and explain that we were going to do a study but none of them were going to be in it. You could have heard a pin drop, and I must admit to feeling a little nervous, but I really admired the way SWAP took it on board and still supported the study. In the end we did include some SWAP members as an 'additional group' in some analyses, particularly those aimed at finding out which types of work had the heaviest exposures.

We found that the former workers still had elevated dioxin levels in their blood twenty years after their exposure to PCP in the sawmills had stopped.[27] Average levels in exposed workers were higher than in the general population, and higher than in non-exposed timber workers (those who didn't work directly with PCP). Some SWAP members had particularly high levels. Dioxin levels increased with length of employment and estimated exposure intensity. So they had definitely had high dioxin exposure, but had it caused any health problems?

We also did a health survey, similar to the one we did for the Dow workers.[28] We found a number of significant associations between PCP exposure levels and various health problems, including tuberculosis, pleurisy or pneumonia, a deficit in cranial nerve function, thyroid disorders, neuropsychological symptoms, heart palpitations and frequent mood changes. The findings were quite convincing because we had done an internal comparison – that is, compared workers who had high PCP exposure with workers in the same mills who had lower exposure. The findings were well received by SWAP, and featured on their website, even though we had not found associations with some of the other health problems they were concerned about.

In fact, our findings were fairly similar to those of the survey that I had been involved in nearly ten years before. So what had changed in that time? I like to think that, despite all the initial problems, we had done the research the right way, and that there was reasonable trust between our group and SWAP. I tried to say all along 'we may not agree on the interpretation of what we find, but let's at least be clear about what we are doing, and why we are doing it'. Certainly I regarded Joe Harawira and other members of SWAP as friends by the time the research finished, and we tried to keep up contact afterwards. In most complex health research efforts there are some disagreements between investigators and other involved individuals.

However, I think another reason the findings were well received was that the issue had dragged on for so long that almost any positive result was regarded as a vindication. In other words, the fact that we had found some (but not all) health problems associated with PCP showed that SWAP had been right to campaign for the previous twenty years against disinterest and obstruction from the companies, the government, DoL and MoH. I tended to agree with them.

5. Where Are We Now?

The more things change. . .

By now, you probably think I wrote this book just to complain about all the difficulties I have experienced in doing these studies. Well, putting the story in print is quite cathartic, and I think it is important to do so – some things happened that are just unacceptable, and if nobody documents them, they are more likely to keep happening. My colleagues in the US have it much worse – those working in this area for government agencies usually need one or more full-time lawyers just to keep the industry and the environmental activists off their backs, and to get their results published despite threats of legal action.

However, I have tried to steer away from simply listing a litany of bad conduct – the book would be much longer if I had documented all the bad stuff that happened. Rather, my main motivation is that very little has changed, and it needs to change. These are not just historical problems. Pesticides are rebranded, sometimes the names of the companies change, the government agencies keep getting reorganised and renamed, but the same problems continue. New Zealand has systemic problems that keep us failing in environmental protection, particularly with regard to pesticides.

New Zealand was one of the last countries in the world (possibly *the* last country) to continue to produce 2,4,5-T and to keep using it after production stopped following the accidental emissions at IWD in 1986.[1] It was the last Western country to use PCP until this ceased in about 1988, and the sawmill workers were the most heavily PCP-exposed group in the world.

Have things improved since the 1980s? A 2020 paper by Andrea 't Mannetje suggests not.[2] She reviewed the data on New Zealand pesticide usage. The most recent available data was from a 2005 report based on a voluntary survey conducted by the New Zealand Association for Animal Health and Crop Protection, supplemented by Statistics New Zealand data on pesticide imports.[3] More reliable, or more recent, data was not available, but there is no reason to believe that things have improved since 2005.

Dr 't Mannetje also compared the classifications of the pesticides according to the New Zealand Environmental Protection Authority (EPA NZ), the EPA US and the European Union (EU). New Zealand's carcinogenicity classifications are less stringent than those of the other two jurisdictions, and many are out of date and don't incorporate the most recent evidence. Although no established human carcinogenic pesticides are currently being used in New Zealand, there is a long list of suspected carcinogens in widespread use. Fifty-six active ingredients are classified as suspected carcinogens, including sixteen high-use ingredients, representing up to 51 per cent of the country's total yearly usage. In 't Mannetje's study, according to the EPA NZ classifications only about 4 per cent of New Zealand pesticide usage involved suspected carcinogens. In contrast, the corresponding figures when using the other two classification systems were 8 per cent (EU) and 26 per cent (EPA US). 't Mannetje commented that many of the pesticides with high use in New Zealand are no longer approved for use in the EU, and that resources for chemical reassessments in small countries such as New Zealand are limited, which is perhaps why the classifications are out of date. For example, the IARC has recently classified glyphosate (more on this later) and 2,4-D (more on this also) as probable or possible carcinogens, but both are still widely used in New Zealand. Moreover, a population survey some colleagues and I carried out on workplace exposure found that 14 per cent of men and 5 per cent of women (10 per cent of workers overall) were exposed to pesticides as part of their work.[4] Exposures were particularly high (63 per cent) in agriculture and fisheries workers.

So how important are these pesticides in terms of the effects on human health? The hazards can sometimes be exaggerated, and people may blame their health problems on the fact that their neighbour sprayed pesticides in the back garden many years ago. Some press reports give the impression that almost any pesticide exposure is hazardous, and that large numbers of people are dying. In fact, most of the risks exist for people who work in manufacturing or spraying the pesticides, and even these are usually small. Risks to the general public are even smaller.

In 2005 I co-authored a paper with 't Mannetje in which we sought to estimate the number of cases of work-related death, disease and injury in New Zealand each year.[5] Overall, we estimated that there were about 100 annual deaths from work-related injury compared with around 700–1,000 from work-related disease. Of these, between 237 and 425 were deaths from cancer. How many of them would be due to pesticides? We don't know, but we are talking about tens of deaths rather than hundreds. There may also be a few from non-cancer causes – diabetes, pesticide poisoning and so on. There is also increasing concern that some pesticides may cause various neurological diseases such as Parkinson's Disease and motor neuron disease. Just as I was finishing this book we published findings from a New Zealand case-control study of motor neuron disease which found increased risks from pesticides (relative risk =1.70), and fumigants (relative risk = 3.98), with risks increasing with longer exposure duration.[6]

These are people with occupational exposures, which tend to be much heavier than those in the general public, so whether there are any cases or deaths among the general public is difficult to judge; if there are, they would be in single figures (but not zero). Of course, none of this excuses our misuse of pesticides, and these numbers are not trivial – I'm just trying to get the problem into perspective. Remember also that pesticides have positive effects – for example, they can help to prevent disease through insect and rodent control.

I have focused on effects on human health in this book, but there is also a concern regarding the effects of these pesticides on the environment – for example, what are neonicotinoids doing to insect diversity?[7] Generally speaking, we do not have a good environmental record. A list of just a few of the recent disasters includes large amounts of toxic waste being stored near the beach at the Tiwai Point aluminium smelter; a tanning company with a history of dumping contaminants down the drain being given a large new contract; increasing levels of nitrates in rivers; and intensive farming damaging native species.[8] There is also continuing concern about the effects of glyphosate on the environment; and the use of 1080 poison has been controversial for decades, although the Parliamentary Commissioner for the Environment concluded in a 2011 report that 1080 is justified in terms of protecting native birds from predators.[9]

Toxic timber treated with copper-chrome-arsenate (CCA) is a growing problem in landfills.[10] CCA has been widely used for decades, particularly for preserving fenceposts. In 1986 I identified that farmers who regularly did fencing work (which almost always involved CCA as the main exposure) had double the usual risk of developing non-Hodgkin's lymphoma; and the treatment is still widely used, particularly for posts in vineyards.[11]

Moreover, there are still thirty or so sites contaminated with PCP, which were identified by Joe Harawira and SWAP. The most significant was perhaps the Kopeopeo Canal in Bay of Plenty, the remediation of which took several years and millions of dollars.[12] Asbestos is another example of an exposure that mainly occurs occupationally but also affects the environment, and on which New Zealand has been incredibly slow to act.[13]

Glyphosate

Glyphosate provides a good example of the challenges of establishing the health effects of pesticides, and the political and economic pressures involved. The world's most widely used herbicide, it is found in about ninety different products in New Zealand. The best known is Roundup, made by Monsanto (now taken over by Bayer).[14] In 2015 the IARC concluded that glyphosate is a 'probable' human carcinogen.[15]

The IARC classifications are the most authoritative internationally. I have participated in several IARC monograph meetings. They involve a group of about fifteen to twenty-five scientists from around the world meeting in Lyon, France, to consider all the available evidence on the carcinogenicity of various agents (usually chemicals). The whole process takes about ten days and is a huge amount of work. Each agent is eventually classified as either carcinogenic (group 1), probably carcinogenic (2A), possibly carcinogenic (2B) or not classifiable (3). The monograph process was recently reviewed in depth and updated, and remains 'state-of-the-art'.[16]

However, the monographs are never far from controversy, mainly because of the financial stakes involved. If a chemical is classified into group 1 (such as TCDD) or group 2A (such as glyphosate), then most governments will take this seriously, and the chemical is subjected to new regulations regarding production or use and may even get phased out. Consequently, some of the classifications, and the IARC processes themselves, have been strongly criticised by industry, and by some scientists with close ties to industry.[17] Because of this, a few years ago I led an ad hoc group of more than 100 scientists who reviewed the processes and the criticisms of those processes.[18] We concluded that the criticisms were unconvincing, and that occasional disagreements among scientists are not evidence of process failure. I don't agree with all the classifications, but then I was usually not there to hear all the evidence, and I recognise that this is the best, most independent and most authoritative system there is.

The controversy over the glyphosate classification was larger than most.[19] In this instance, in my opinion, there was a concerted effort from industry, similar to the approaches used by the tobacco industry, to attack not only the IARC conclusions but also the scientists involved.[20] In reaction, I wrote a blog for the London School of Hygiene and Tropical Medicine (LSHTM) website entitled 'Independent, Rigorous, Vilified – Why Attacks on the International Agency for Research on Cancer Are Unfair'.[21] It noted that there had been

attacks not only on the IARC [glyphosate] decision, but also on some of those involved in the IARC Monograph meeting which made the decision, and on IARC itself. These events are not happening in a vacuum. There have been attacks on previous IARC decisions on potential causes of cancer such as formaldehyde, diesel fumes and radiofrequency electromagnetic field. More ominously, there are moves by some governments to threaten to cut the funding of IARC, in response to these recent 'inconvenient' decisions. [This was the Trump era.]

This drew the inevitable response: industry attacked not only the IARC, but me personally.[22]

Unfortunately, these sorts of attacks are not unusual. I describe them in detail in a book I wrote about my experience in discovering that an asthma drug (fenoterol) was causing an epidemic of asthma deaths in New Zealand, and I have also discussed these issues in various academic papers.[23] It is not surprising that scientists often disagree – see what has happened with Covid-19, over issues such as mask-wearing.[24] That's why we need agencies such as the IARC to assemble groups of scientists from different disciplines with no conflicts of interest to review the data in depth. As I said in my LSHTM piece:

[W]e all look up to IARC and see it as a beacon of independence and objectivity in a world which is becoming increasingly partisan and polarised, and in which scientific evidence is increasingly disparaged and ignored. Facts matter, science matters, and in this field, there is no other agency which even comes close to IARC in terms of independence, objectivity, and transparency.

But of course, not everybody agrees. In response to the IARC report, the European Food Safety Authority (EFSA) produced a rival report concluding that 'the overall weight of evidence does not indicate that glyphosate is carcinogenic'.[25] The reasons for the differences between the IARC and EFSA evaluations were critically reviewed by Portier et al. (this is Chris Portier who led the Vietnam visit I was involved in – see Chapter 2), who noted a number of shortcomings in the EFSA approach.[26]

It also became apparent that the EFSA report had relied heavily on non-peer reviewed industry-funded studies that were not publicly available (the IARC can only use publicly available information for its assessments); that employees of Monsanto had ghost-written papers published in the scientific literature that claimed to be from 'independent' scientists; and that the report included analyses copied and pasted from a Monsanto study report.[27] These shortcomings eventually prompted EFSA to create a panel, on which I served, to provide guidance on appraising and integrating evidence from epidemiological studies for use in the authority's scientific assessments.[28] This will hopefully improve future processes and reports, but so far it has not led to a re-evaluation of the glyphosate report. At the time of writing, EFSA was in fact considering the renewal of glyphosate's registration, which had only been extended for five years in the previous evaluation.[29]

So where does the EPA NZ come into this? Well, it rejected the IARC expert assessment and produced its own report, written by a single author with input from one other scientist, neither of whom had epidemiological training.[30] It reached similar conclusions to the flawed EFSA report, namely that 'glyphosate is unlikely to be carcinogenic to humans and does not require classification under HSNO [the Hazardous Substances and New Organisms Act 1996] as a carcinogen or mutagen'. This was despite even MoH advising that it would be 'reluctant to criticise any [IARC] classification based on the review of one individual'.[31] In subsequent publications, the EPA NZ's chief scientist cited a Reuters article attacking the chair of the IARC panel, and hinting that the evaluation was invalid.[32]

The chief scientist subsequently noted that the EPA NZ agreed with the IARC that cancer could occur at high exposures and dosages, but added, 'we don't have these high exposures and dosages in New Zealand'.[33] However, that is a completely different issue, and illustrates a problem to which I will return in the final chapter. The EPA NZ concedes that glyphosate may cause cancer at high doses, but assumes – without any evidence, since there is no data on typical exposure levels – that these high-level exposures don't occur in New Zealand. Even if they don't, this doesn't change the fact that glyphosate may cause cancer. The focus of the IARC monographs is on whether the substance can cause cancer – they don't consider what dose levels are required (though in fact, neither does the EPA NZ). However, rather than 'alarming the public' by conceding that glyphosate may be carcinogenic (and that, therefore, at the very least, we should try and keep exposures as low as possible), the EPA NZ simply refuses to concede that it could be carcinogenic at all.

The pressures such agencies face are typified by a Spinoff article by Nick Stringer, who notes that unacceptable traces of glyphosate in New Zealand honey have led Japan to threaten to stop importing it.[34] On the other hand, there are strong pressures from the agricultural sector (as there were for 2,4,5-T and PCP) to keep using it, because it is cheap, easy to apply and comparatively nontoxic (in the sense that it is unlikely to cause acute health problems such as overdose). We rely on agencies such as the EPA NZ to speak truth to power, and to lay out the scientific evidence as objectively as possible. Politicians and the public can then decide what to do – such as ban it or keep using it while trying to keep exposure as low as possible. The authority is failing in environmental protection when it ignores the decisions of agencies such as the IARC, buys into industry narratives, and ignores inconvenient scientific evidence.

2,4-D

The scientific case against 2,4-D is perhaps not as strong as that against glyphosate, but the way the issue has been handled in New Zealand is just as bizarre. 2,4-D is a phenoxy herbicide that was used in Agent Orange, together with 2,4,5-T (see Chapter 2). Like 2,4,5-T, it has been used since the 1940s to control broadleaf weeds. Unlike 2,4,5-T, it has not been banned and is still widely used. As recently as 2016, the Ministry for the Environment website stated:

> The herbicide 2,4-D, which is contaminated with small amounts of dioxin, is still used in New Zealand. However, the dioxin inventory estimated that this pesticide is a relatively minor source of all dioxin released to the environment. The Pesticides Board recently looked at the use of 2,4-D in New Zealand and decided not to prohibit its use.[35]

The 2020 paper by 't Mannetje listed 2,4-D as one of the sixteen high-use pesticides where the active ingredient was a possible human carcinogen.[36]

Attention has always focused on 2,4,5-T, since this contains TCDD, the most toxic form of dioxin. However, most studies of phenoxy herbicides (the group to which 2,4,5-T and 2,4-D belong) have also examined 2,4-D. The main type of cancer that seemed to have an increased incidence from exposure to it was non-Hodgkin's lymphoma. In fact, non-Hodgkin's lymphoma studies I did in New Zealand in the 1980s did not indicate much of a risk.[37] However, they had limited exposure data (we just asked people what chemicals they had used, and what they had been spraying), and a study we published in 2007 did show higher risks for agricultural occupations where pesticide exposure (particularly 2,4-D) was likely.[38] Overall, the evidence against 2,4-D is not overwhelming, but it was sufficient for the IARC to classify it as a possible (group 2B) human carcinogen in 2015.[39]

In 2003 I was contacted by the Environmental Risk Management Authority (ERMA), which later became the EPA NZ. The creation of the ERMA, and the transfer of thousands of chemicals to a new classification under the HSNO Act, had given 2,4-D manufacturers a new chance to dispute the classification. The ERMA was proposing that 2,4-D be classified as 6.7B – substances that are suspected human carcinogens – which roughly corresponded to the IARC 2B classification.

The ERMA had received a submission from Nufarm Australia, an Australian agricultural chemical company headquartered in Melbourne that held more than 2,100 product registrations and marketed products in more than 100 countries. In particular, it was a manufacturer of phenoxy herbicides, including 2,4-D. The submission seemed to be based on two arguments: (i) other expert committees had subsequently reviewed the evidence and come to different conclusions than the IARC; and (ii) more recent evidence put forward in a paper by Manolis Kogevinas et al. had related the increased risks from phenoxy herbicides to dioxin contamination, and was not relevant to current production.[40] Therefore phenoxy herbicides should be classified as 'not a carcinogen' under the HSNO Act (although in fact, this particular classification does not exist under the legislation).[41]

The ERMA asked me to comment on this claim about the paper by Kogevinas et al., since I was a co-author of the paper (it included my New Zealand phenoxy herbicide production cohort).[42] In fact the paper does conclude that the risks are higher for, and could even be restricted to, phenoxy herbicides that are contaminated with TCDD (which 2,4-D is not), but it doesn't present separate findings for 2,4-D and definitely doesn't give it a clean bill of health. Certainly, the evidence that TCDD is carcinogenic is much stronger than the evidence for 2,4-D – which is why TCDD is in group 1 (sufficient evidence of carcinogenicity), whereas 2,4-D is only in group 2B (possible carcinogen). In its submission, Dow AgroSciences also claimed that the risks were solely for TCDD, citing a more recent paper by David McLean and myself, in which we had actually concluded the opposite, that the increased risks from phenoxy herbicides did not appear to be confined to the ones containing TCDD, and might be due to phenoxy herbicides themselves rather than the dioxin contaminants.[43]

I already knew that some other official committees

had come to different conclusions from the IARC. This was hardly news (see the story of glyphosate above) and was not a reason to change the ERMA classification, since the IARC was widely regarded as the definitive agency for making such classifications. I was more puzzled by the reference to the Kogevinas et al. paper, since I was a co-author and I knew that it contained nothing new about 2,4-D. It was about phenoxy herbicides in general, and it was difficult to separate the effects of 2,4-D (which, in any case, contains some types of dioxin) from those of dioxins. The IARC classification had not been based just on this particular study, but on the overall range of epidemiological, animal and mechanistic evidence. The fact that a particular study, albeit the largest and best one available, had been updated was not a reason to change the classification, particularly since this new publication had nothing specifically on 2,4-D.

Nevertheless, the ERMA changed its classification in response to the industry submissions, and against my advice as a co-author of the key paper. So 2,4-D continues to be classified as 'not a carcinogen' under the HSNO Act and continues to be widely used in New Zealand. I'm not disputing the ERMA decision itself – few countries have actually banned 2,4-D, although a number restrict its use in various ways. But I was staggered by how easily the ERMA was prepared to change the classification based on a particular study, which I know did not show what the industry submissions claimed it showed. As usual, there appeared to be little or no epidemiological input to the decision, apart from my own small and ineffective contribution.

6. So How Do We Fix It?

The story of pesticides in New Zealand is a paradigm of the problems of dealing with environmental hazards. It is usually only after long campaigns that the affected communities are given some support – and the decisions about this are usually motivated by politics, economic issues and community pressure rather than the real risks.

For example: (i) Vietnam veterans actually had very low exposure to TCDD, but after many years of campaigning were granted a parliamentary inquiry, an official apology from the government, and some compensation; (ii) residents of Paritutū, the suburb near the IWD factory, had higher exposure to TCDD, and after many years of campaigning were eventually tested and given some additional health services; but (iii) after many years of campaigning, workers with very high exposure to TCDD (those at the IWD plant, timber workers and others) have had very little help from the government. Initially, there was not even any recognition of an occupational exposure problem, although the MoH support service did eventually cover people occupationally exposed.[1]

This is not to say that Vietnam veterans should not have been compensated, but it does show that other communities with much greater exposure are being neglected. The reasons are complex, but it is hard to avoid the conclusion that the veterans have good political clout and community support, that residents of affected communities have less political support, and marginalised groups of workers, including former timber workers based in Māori communities, have little political leverage. The Welsh general practice researcher Julian Tudor Hart has proposed the 'inverse care law', namely, that the availability of good medical care tends to vary inversely with the need of the population served.[2] We perhaps see a similar 'inverse community care law' whereby the communities most affected by pesticide exposure get the least help and political recognition.

What happened with pesticides, particularly those containing dioxin, has happened with many other environmental hazards, and there are lessons to be learned about how we deal, or don't deal, with such controversies in future. I'll start by discussing the questionable roles of the government agencies involved.

Ministry of Health

In 1900 New Zealand was one of the first countries to establish a national Department of Public Health. It initially focused on disease prevention and health promotion; in 1903, however, it became the Department of Health and, as in most Western countries, evolved into a focus on medical care services with some prevention functions. The more recent evolution of MoH in its various guises is covered in an excellent book by Professor David Skegg (*The Health of the People*), which in part inspired me to write this BWB Text.[3]

When I first started doing health research in 1980, there was still a Department of Health. Its renaming as the Ministry of Health in the 1990s signified a major shift, although it perhaps only accelerated changes that had begun happening during the 1980s. The department's central monitoring functions (for example, the Cancer Registry and the monitoring of deaths and hospital admissions) had been allowed to decline. This decline was accelerated with the shift to area health boards, now called district health boards. These took up a large share of the funding, with the central department/ministry fulfilling more of a policy role rather than delivering services. The area health boards quickly diverted much of their public health funding into treatment services. This was perhaps not surprising, given the daily pressure to shorten waiting lists and provide urgent services – these are always going to win out over the longer-term, and often less newsworthy, benefits of health protection and promotion.

This problem typified a debate that has been going on for as long as I have been involved in public health. Advocates of 'turning the health services into public health services' saw potential for reorienting the massive health budget into health protection and promotion, with a focus on improved healthy lifestyles rather than occupational and environmental factors. This approach, unfortunately in my view, was also supported by the Labour Party, and Helen Clark in particular (whom I have great respect for in general, but whose approach on this issue I don't agree with). It also strongly influenced WHO policy, led by a small number of New Zealanders, on prevention of non-communicable disease, with an emphasis on individual lifestyle (smoking, drinking, diet, exercise and so on) and the neglect of environmental influences on health (air pollution, soil and water contamination, urban design and so on).[4] This attitude comes through repeatedly when MoH is required to deal with environmental health issues (as seen at Paritutū, and with the timber workers). Usually, the responsible officials have little training, and even less interest, in these issues. They tend to regard them as trivial, try to do as little as possible, and hope the problem will go away. This lack of interest is easily seen by the public, who lose confidence in the officials and start to disbelieve everything they say. 'People don't care how much you know until they know how much you care.'[5]

Others, including myself, argued that public health would always miss out in this context ('a very small tail trying to wag a very large dog'), and that it was better for public health to have a separate authority – this approach is well established in the US, for example, where different government agencies oversee health care delivery (Medicare and Medicaid) and prevention at the population level (Centers for Disease Control and Prevention).[6] To my surprise, this actually happened briefly during the 1990s, due to the National government's health sector reform. As David Skegg documents, members of the government taskforce for the reorganisation were convinced that public health was being neglected, and recommended the separation of the funding and management of population-based health services from personal health care services.[7] They also recommended the creation of the Public Health Commission (PHC), which Skegg chaired from its establishment in 1992.

During its first few years, the PHC produced two excellent annual reports, the first comprehensive reports on the health of New Zealanders for many years. As well as the major problems, it identified factors affecting population health, including social inequalities, environmental conditions, hazardous substances and waste management.[8] It also produced a discussion document, 'Towards Healthy Lives for New Zealanders', mapping the path forward for population health. The PHC's eighth (and final) newsletter included policy advice on alcohol, cervical cancer, child hearing loss, food safety, nutrition, hazardous substances, HIV/AIDS, immunisation, melanoma, road traffic injuries, sudden infant death syndrome, tobacco, water quality, water safety, congenital and inherited conditions, Māori health, Pasifika health, parenting, school health, the local environment and oral health.[9]

I only had a small involvement with the PHC, but many friends and colleagues worked for it, or with it. Notably, it functioned much more like similar institutions in the US, and to some extent the UK, where government agencies – for example, the US National Cancer Institute, the EPA US, the NIEHS and Public Health England (now the UK Health Security Agency) – focus on policy-relevant research. They can convey the evidence at any given time to policymakers, who then make the best judgements they can, taking the evidence into account. These agencies include career researchers, who often hold joint appointments with universities, or move back and forth between the two roles. Skegg comments on the infectious atmosphere 'in which people worked extremely hard to raise the profile and performance of public health'.[10] These were real scientists with specialist expertise, not just generic policy analysts. It was a rare 'interregnum' in the continuing decline of public health expertise in government.

It was too good to last, and it didn't. The PHC's draft reports angered the Dairy Board, the Beer, Wine and Spirits Council and the Wine Institute, and its mere existence angered MoH, which had previously had this role. It made so many enemies (including the food industry) that it was abolished after three years and merged back into the ministry. Skegg describes in depressing detail the series of meetings with ministers and MoH officials that led to the PHC's abolition.[11]

None of MoH's regular reorganisations since then appear to have enhanced the profile, funding or independence of public health. Subsequent governments (both National and then Labour) did create a Public Health Group within the ministry, as well as a National Health Committee and a related Public Health Advisory Committee. I served on both committees between 2002 and 2007, and we produced some useful reports. However, we had little real power, and the work of the two committees was tightly controlled by the MoH secretariat.[12] Our report on chronic disease contained a section on the highly successful Wairarapa Māori Asthma Project, which I had co-led.[13] MoH was not keen on this project, since the ministry's funding model was not consistent with the project's strong Māori community involvement

– at least four times I inserted the section into the report, only to have it removed by the secretariat. In the end, a much-shortened section was included.

As I write this book, another restructuring of MoH is under way.[14] How this will pan out is unclear, but once again there appears to be little sign of public health having more funding or independence.[15] In particular, it appears that the creation of a Public Health Agency in the ministry is simply rebranding the Public Health Group, and it will likely suffer the same fate. The group – established when the PHC was disestablished – was initially led by a second-tier manager with its budget and expenditure identified in MoH's annual report. This lasted for a couple of years before the group sank down the hierarchy, with only one resurgence, before disappearing altogether from the ministry's organisational chart. The various public health units are now being placed into the new national agency Health New Zealand. Thus, both at ministry and service delivery level, public health will continue to lack independence, or even a transparent and discoverable agenda, and will remain at the mercy of political influences – still at risk of being cut to provide more funding for personal health services and to reduce waiting lists.

WorkSafe

At the time of the Paritutū dioxin controversy, I wrote a short piece for the Public Health Association newsletter entitled 'Who Cares about Occupational Health?'[16] It was prompted by the bizarre situation whereby the Public

Health Directorate of MoH was responsible for the community exposures but not for those of the workers. At the same time, OSH (then a branch of DoL) denied responsibility for the workers since the exposures had occurred before OSH's creation in 1992. I noted that I should accept some of the blame for the situation since I was one of many people (occupational health specialists, unions, researchers and others) who supported the creation of OSH. Many of us felt that occupational health was not being given enough priority by MoH, and that there was a lack of coordination between MoH, DoL and other agencies. The 1984–90 Labour government therefore set up a review of the administration of occupational health and safety, and a tripartite advisory council recommended new legislation – which became the Health and Safety in Employment Act 1992 – plus the establishment of both an enforcement agency (OSH) and a separate policy, strategy and research institute. The separate institute was never established. The resources and responsibility for occupational health were transferred from MoH to OSH, which became the occupational health equivalent of the Public Health Directorate in the ministry.

OSH, however, focused on occupational injury and did little for occupational health, despite the motivation and good intentions of many excellent staff. This does not reflect any shortcomings in the Act, or in the structure of OSH. Rather, it reflects shortcomings in the corporate culture of OSH, which never successfully made the transition from being the safety and regulatory arm of DoL to being an organisation concerned with health as well as safety. In fact, it allowed the specialist occupational health resource that had been moved from MoH to diminish through attrition over time. Some OSH district offices, after less than ten years, had no remaining occupational medicine specialists or occupational nurses. So OSH simply didn't have the resources or expertise to cope with situations like Paritutū or the ongoing controversy about PCP.

The final stage in this process of 'death by a thousand cuts' occurred when OSH was quietly disestablished and incorporated into the Workplace Group of DoL, together with the Industrial Relations Service and the department's ACC responsibilities. The OSH name and brand rapidly disappeared. Like the PHC, which MoH wanted to absorb and neutralise, DoL wanted to absorb and neutralise OSH.

At this time it was argued by some that OSH didn't provide occupational health services but instead focused on prevention and therefore didn't need specialist occupational health expertise. However, you can't do effective prevention of occupational disease (just as you can't do effective public health prevention) unless your team includes health care professionals who know about health and disease and can provide advice and support to those whom prevention has failed. If you only have bureaucrats and inspectors, then you can deal with someone cutting their hand off in a circular saw but not with complex problems like Paritutū or PCP. OSH sometimes argued that it didn't have to deal with such problems because once people get sick they are solely MoH's responsibility. However, it was clear that the responsibility for such occupational health problems (both before and after they happen) had been transferred to OSH, which is why MoH was helping the community but not the workers.

I was on a series of government advisory committees for occupational health and safety during this time, but none of them seemed able to shift the intransigence and neglect of DoL or MoH with regard to occupational health. These committees included the Occupational Health Technical Advisory Committee to the Minister of Health (1988–91), the ACC Advisory Panel on Work Related Gradual Process, Disease or Infection (2001–19), and the MoH Organochlorines Technical Advisory Group (around 2001–10). All struggled with the difficulties of protection against the long-term effects of environmental and occupational exposure. DoL and ACC were much more concerned about preventing workplace injuries, whereas MoH was more concerned about changing individual lifestyles (eat better, exercise more, don't smoke) than about dealing with difficult and controversial issues such as pesticide exposure.

My old research group at Massey University held a national symposium on occupational health and safety in 2002 (this was part of a more general symposium series, which included the dioxin symposium in 2005), and the Minister of Labour at the time, Margaret Wilson, opened the meeting.[17] Subsequently, she established the National Occupational Safety and Health Advisory Committee (NOHSAC), which I chaired until it was abolished by the new National government in 2009. Wilson was clear that it was established to provide her with a second stream of advice – in other words, to bypass the bad advice she was getting from DoL. We produced a series of reports that were largely ignored by DoL, and by successive ministers who were perhaps less enthusiastic about preventing occupational disease than Wilson was.[18] The first, and perhaps most influential, report estimated that there were 700–1,000 deaths each year from occupational disease, in addition to about 100 from occupational injury.[19] Subsequent reports included surveillance of occupational disease, surveillance and control of workplace exposures, the economic and social costs of workplace disease and injury, the profile of occupational health and safety, the efficacy of various instruments, the evolving work environment, work-related harm, and occupational health and safety in small businesses and for women.[20] At the time I took the attitude that we were in this for the long haul and that the reports would eventually begin to influence long-term policy even if ignored when first published. This turned out to be the case.

An Independent Taskforce on Workplace Health and Safety was established in 2012, partly in response to the 2010 Pike River mine disaster. Its 2013 report raised similar issues to those in the profile mentioned above.[21] It concluded that 'New Zealand's current health and safety system is not fit for purpose' and recommended the establishment of a new workplace health and safety agency 'with a clear identity and brand'. Most of the detailed recommendations focused on occupational injury, but it was noted (referencing our NOHSAC reports and workplace exposure surveys[22]) that

New Zealand's estimated 500–800 premature deaths each year from occupational ill-health receive little government, media or business attention. Inadequate data systems and research mean the scale and nature of the issues are largely unknown – and the system is unresponsive to new and emerging risks.

The report went on to recommend that the agency should have 'a unit dedicated to this area of risk' and that it urgently needed to 'build an occupational health serious harm dataset and facilitate the development of whole-of-life databases ... it should have the powers to require an employer or a medical provider to provide to it anonymised health-monitoring information on request'.

The new agency, WorkSafe New Zealand, was established in 2013, and now has more than 550 staff throughout the country. So far, there is no sign of the dedicated occupational health unit that was recommended. On the other hand, there is increasing activity in occupational health, and a strategic plan for work-related health, with a number of different teams involved. Frequent reference is made to the NOHSAC reports, and there's a particular emphasis on reducing workplace exposures. There also appear to be genuine efforts to increase epidemiological and public health expertise, and I do hear good comments about some of the developments from friends and colleagues who are involved. This is promising, although it is also of concern that this work apparently has time-limited funding rather than being part of ongoing core funding. Priorities include carcinogens (including pesticides), airborne risks, musculoskeletal disorders, mentally healthy work, inequities and psychosocial factors at work, as well as work-related health surveillance.

So this is progress, but some problems remain, particularly regarding the need for a dedicated occupational health unit, and ongoing core funding for this activity. Issues also remain as to who is responsible for occupational health monitoring (for example, WorkSafe, MoH, ACC), while provision of health services related to occupational exposures appears still to be primarily the responsibility of MoH.

One theme to which I will return is the methods and skills involved in promoting occupational and environmental health: they are quite different from those involved in injury prevention, and perhaps it is not feasible to integrate them in the same organisation, although WorkSafe is clearly trying. One objection to occupational health coming under another agency is that it would clearly be inefficient and disruptive to have two sets of inspectors from different agencies visiting the same workplaces. And I should admit that many of my colleagues involved in occupational health and safety think it would be logistically impractical to separate out occupational health and injury at the 'factory level'.

On the other hand, the key occupational health activities generally occur at a higher level (for example, regulation of carcinogens, population monitoring of occupational disease), and there are agencies (such as the defunct PHC) that much more clearly have, or had, the specialist expertise. So, it would not be impossible to have a single set of inspectors, with an organisation such as WorkSafe embedded in a broader agency (see my comments on the PHC) to provide broader policy and regulatory expertise.

New Zealand Environmental Protection Authority

The key legislation for management of pesticide risks is the HSNO Act. When this became law in 1996, it was noted that New Zealand had been without a national surveillance system on poisonings and other chemical injuries for more than ten years. There were attempts by ESR to create such a system, as required under the HSNO Act.[23] At the time, it was noted that there were about 5,000 poisonings or injuries from chemicals resulting in hospitalisations, about 80 deaths from accidental chemical poisonings, and about 200 from intentional self-poisoning.[24]

The government agency responsible for implementing the HSNO Act was the ERMA, which was established under the Act and existed until 2011, when it was replaced by the EPA NZ. The ERMA's main aim was to 'achieve effective prevention or management of risks to the environment, public health and safety associated with importing or manufacturing hazardous substances and introducing new organisms and their use'. The EPA NZ has similar aims; its 2019/20 report notes that its role 'is to regulate the use of hazardous substances and new organisms to ensure they are safe to be used'. The report also notes that New Zealand's hazardous substances database is being replaced with a new classification system known as the Globally Harmonised System

Version 7 (GHS 7), which is an internationally agreed way of classifying chemicals based on their human and environmental hazards.

The main issue of concern with the EPA NZ, as with the ERMA, is the availability and mix of scientific expertise. In Chapter 5, I noted that the EPA NZ's review of glyphosate was done by one person, with one advisor, neither of whom had training in epidemiology. This hardly gives us confidence for the future.

'The experts can't agree'

A chronic difficulty for government agencies is expert disagreement. Just as not all experts can agree about the best strategies to combat Covid-19, there are genuine disagreements about the safety of pesticides. These are very apparent in the perpetual disputes about the IARC classifications. The 'solution' is to take the same approach that the IARC does, that is, to get together a committee of experts who have no conflicts of interest and who span the relevant disciplines. There are obvious difficulties in doing this in a small country because of the wide breadth of expertise required. For this reason, it is questionable whether New Zealand should be trying to do its own assessments, which might run counter to the international gold standards such as those of the IARC.[25] At the very least, New Zealand's assessments need to be done by comprehensive interdisciplinary committees, with the involvement of overseas experts, rather than the ludicrous approach taken with glyphosate.

There are two main kinds of expert disagreement.

The first is between different types of experts. Most commonly, arguments about pesticide safety happen between toxicologists and epidemiologists. Toxicology is the science of the adverse effects of chemicals on living organisms, including humans – for instance, can it poison or kill you? It is an essential science with regard to pesticide safety, and I have great respect for what toxicologists do; unfortunately, they don't always have great respect for what I do. The problem is that some chemicals that appear to be hazardous show up in epidemiological studies but not in toxicology studies.

For example, for some years it was clear from epidemiological studies that arsenic could cause cancer, but it took many years for that to be confirmed in toxicological studies.[26] The likely reason is that arsenic is not a direct mutagen (making changes in DNA); rather, it probably knocks out the enzyme systems that repair damage to DNA. Under this scenario, arsenic would cause cancer not on its own (for example, if you just fed arsenic to a rat) but only in combination with another carcinogen (which can occur in free-living humans). More generally, if a new chemical is found to be a mutagen, or to cause cancer in laboratory animals, then in Western countries it won't be marketed and used. However, we keep finding new causes of cancer, which therefore involve new mechanisms not yet thought of by toxicologists. These epidemiological findings usually then get attacked by toxicologists, and the controversy may continue for some years.

I have been on more committees than I would care to remember (I am on one now in the UK) that have involved strong arguments between the two groups, with the epidemiologists frequently outnumbered. Usually, epidemiology is dismissed as 'only showing association, not causation' (how, then, did we establish that smoking causes lung cancer?) In general, toxicology studies of potential carcinogens involve carefully controlled experimental designs in the wrong species (not humans), whereas epidemiological studies are observational rather than experimental but in the right species (humans). Each approach has strengths and weaknesses, but together they can be synergistic and powerful.

In New Zealand, the ACC panel established in 1998 to deal with claims related to PCP and phenoxy herbicides is called the 'Toxicology Panel'. Its members are not without epidemiological expertise, but it is striking that such an important panel does not explicitly include epidemiology in its title or membership. In contrast, a similar council (albeit one dealing with general recommendations rather than individual cases) – the one of which I'm a member in the UK – contains a much broader range of expertise, including epidemiology.

Another kind of disagreement occurs between epidemiologists as to which types of evidence are most reliable.[27] Briefly, these experts fall into two schools. The first regards the randomised controlled trial as the 'gold standard' and dismisses or strongly downgrades evidence from most observational studies. In recent years, attempts have been made to 'score' epidemiological studies according to how closely they mimic randomised controlled trial methodology.[28] As a result, most of the evidence is usually discarded, leaving the authors to conclude that 'there is no evidence of risk'.[29] The other school (to which I belong) argues that it is not as simple as that, that there is no perfect study, but that we need to put all the evidence together, using a variety of study designs, and 'triangulate' before reaching a conclusion – which is essentially what the IARC does.[30] This approach is essential in situations where it would be unethical or impossible to do a randomised trial – we can't purposely expose people to toxins such as cigarette smoke or pesticides.

These disputes between experts occur in the context of heavy pressure from industry, particularly over pesticide safety. I have already documented some of this pressure with regard to dioxin, glyphosate, 2,4-D and so on, in earlier chapters, and I and others have written extensively about their effect on the practice of epidemiology.[31]

What definitely doesn't work is holding an official inquiry and discussing individual cases. It creates headlines but tells you almost nothing. This is not to say we should not have such inquiries – they give the public important opportunities to speak and to document what has happened to them. It's just that it's not a way to provide scientific answers. If you take any group of adult New Zealanders, a significant proportion will have health problems. Similarly, about 2–3 per cent of all pregnancies result in congenital malformations, and a much higher proportion (15–30 per cent) in miscarriages. So, if there are lots of submissions from Vietnam veterans who have had health problems (cancer, diabetes and so on), what does this mean? They will almost all have friends and family of the same age who didn't go to Vietnam but who have had the same problems. Epidemiological studies are the only way of finding out if a particular group has more health problems than people of the same age who didn't have the same exposure. This is how it was established that smoking causes lung cancer, that asbestos causes lung cancer and mesothelioma, that radiation causes most types of cancer, that thalidomide causes birth defects, and so on.

'The experts can't be trusted'

The next problem is how these expert opinions are used by policymakers and reported. Typically, when a new hazard arises, or new concern about an existing hazard, there is very little information on which to make a judgement. Some would argue that we should apply the 'precautionary principle', and that a hazard should be removed or exposure minimised, even if the evidence is weak, until better evidence becomes available.[32] The problem is that virtually everything we are exposed to – every chemical, every type of food, most types of smoke – has some 'evidence' of being hazardous (just pick an exposure at random and google it). Most of this 'evidence' is just random noise. It's only when you get fairly consistent evidence from more than one study, or strong evidence from a single superior study, that you might conclude that the association is causal.

Naturally, in the early years of concern about a hazard, consistent evidence from multiple studies will not be available. Usually, then, the relevant regulatory or policy

122

authorities will review the evidence, conclude that it is very weak and preliminary, and that increased risk has not been proved (nor has no risk at all, but this is usually not mentioned). In practice, this 'lack of convincing evidence' gets escalated into policy statements and press statements that 'there is no evidence that xxx is dangerous' or even that 'xxx is safe'. The informal rationale for this is usually along the lines of 'we don't want to alarm the public' or 'the public can't handle it'. What they really mean is that the authorities can't handle being honest about our uncertainty. And because of this refusal to admit that we don't know, the public lose faith in scientists and policymakers.

Then, over the following years, as the evidence accumulates, the authorities tend to support their original conclusions. This continues until the evidence is overwhelming and authorities in other parts of the world take action. Eventually, New Zealand does as well.

Take TCDD. Concern about this first arose during the Vietnam War period, and then in the early 1980s in New Zealand, because we had the highest usage of 2,4,5-T per capita in the world, and were one of the last countries still producing it.[33] At the time, the Agricultural Chemicals Board issued a number of statements that '2,4,5-T is safe' (I heard board representatives say that at a public meeting in 1980). A series of presentations at the Royal Society that year involved experts in the chemistry, pharmacology and human genetics of 2,4,5-T, but not an epidemiologist – possibly because at the time they had few if any fellows who were epidemiologists (when I became a fellow in 2005, there were still very few).[34] The synopsis of the presentations concluded that 'there are few grounds for regarding 2,4,5-T itself as having any important health hazards'[35] – although it did at least concede that 'where any shadow of doubt remains, epidemiologic studies should be performed'.[36]

A Department of Health report in 1985 also concluded that 'the overwhelming evidence for the safety of the use and manufacture of 2,4,5-T leads to the question of why the concern and allegations have persisted'.[37] Around the same time, the leading Department of Health official in occupational health appeared on television saying that 2,4,5-T was 'so safe that you could drink it'.[38] The ministerial committee of inquiry mentioned in Chapter 3 reached similar conclusions about safety in 1986, but did raise some issues for further consideration.[39] In the same year, the Pesticides Board decided to halve the number of 2,4,5-T tests for TCDD contamination, and rely on tests done by the company.[40] The Department of Health eventually had to respond to accusations of bias – its independence was questioned in an Environmental Council report – but did not change its approach.[41] Production of 2,4,5-T in New Plymouth ceased in 1987 following the industrial accident in 1986 and the ministerial committee report.[42] The first publication from the definitive IARC cohort, showing a 30 per cent overall increased risk of cancer, appeared in 1991, and six years later the IARC classified TCDD as a carcinogen.[43]

All of this is perhaps reasonable, and probably unavoidable, in terms of how long science takes to reach definitive conclusions. The issue is what you do in the meantime.

This is particularly so with chemicals such as TCDD, since they persist in the environment, and in people's bodies for a very long time (the half-life of TCDD in the body is about 10 years), so failure to act quickly can have serious long-term consequences for both the environment and human health.

Claiming that there is no risk is dishonest and alienates the public. As Gwenda Paul and Joe Harawira from SWAP said:

> The people have been sitting in their community, watching what has been going on for many years, trying to make their concerns known, but nobody will listen. By the time somebody does listen they are past being reasonable. Of course this makes people back off and say, 'Oh these people are just angry, just out of it, we can't deal with these people'. But that is why they are so angry. The authorities always come into the picture too late.[44]

We are now seeing the consequences of this approach, not just for pesticides but globally in terms of vaccine and Covid-19 scepticism. Of course, nothing justifies the bizarre and extreme beliefs of the Covid-19 deniers, the anti-vaxxers, or those who blame every health problem on pesticide exposure. However, these extreme and often absurd views represent the far end of a continuum of more generally reduced levels of public trust in scientists and policymakers. When scientists and policymakers say what they think the government wants them to say, rather than speaking openly and admitting when they are unsure about the evidence, the public quickly sees through this and their level of trust in government and scientists is reduced. What goes around comes around.

So how do we fix it?

We have plenty of examples of what not to do, and some of what can be achieved. Let's first list the problems, before considering possible solutions.

A large number of government agencies have different, and sometimes conflicting, responsibilities for environmental and occupational health. This was typified by the Paritutū dioxin fiasco. What happens currently in terms of pesticides? The EPA NZ is responsible for approving their use. WorkSafe is then responsible for the safety of the workers, particularly for the short-term (acute) effects of pesticide poisoning. In theory it is also responsible for the long-term effects, but currently lacks the expertise for monitoring those. The Ministry for the Environment is responsible for the environmental effects – such as when pesticide runoff from farms contaminates rivers – but regional councils are responsible for keeping to the standards set by the ministry, and there appears to be much shifting of responsibility and blame.[45] MoH is responsible for the health effects on the population, but has limited public health expertise (or at least less than the PHC had), very little environmental health expertise, and virtually no occupational health expertise. In theory, it is also responsible for monitoring the long-term effects on the population.

There is inadequate, and dwindling, expertise in the

government agencies that deal with environmental and occupational health generally, and pesticides in particular.

The creation of the position of Parliamentary Commissioner for the Environment in 1986 was a positive move – the current commissioner is Simon Upton, a former environment and health minister. However, his office has little or no health expertise.

The Ministry for the Environment continues to produce comprehensive assessments of the state of the environment, although with little information on health effects, and only occasional mention of pesticides.[46] Issues identified include deteriorating water quality and gaps in monitoring. In particular, New Zealand lags behind many Western countries in that it has only just started monitoring PM2.5 (fine particulate matter – a key measure of air pollution) and doesn't yet routinely monitor NO_2 (nitrogen dioxide – a major component of car exhaust).[47] Related to this are the weak controls on vehicle emissions.[48] In contrast, the Zero Carbon Act and the Climate Change Commission are positive developments.

Public health in general remains a low priority for MoH, and environmental health remains a low priority within public health. Occupational health does not feature at all. As David Skegg notes, there is a long list of activities that have been moved out of MoH over the years, including food safety (now in the Ministry for Primary Industries), occupational health and safety (WorkSafe), the immunisation schedule (Pharmac), hazardous substances (the EPA NZ) and infectious disease surveillance and outbreak investigation (ESR).[49] Unfortunately, with MoH the more things change the more they stay the same, and I see little hope that it can be revitalised to take a leading role in environmental health (Skegg cites a former PHC employee who asked 'do I get a free lobotomy when I rejoin the ministry?').

Wherever public health is based, one wonders whether it can effectively tackle environmental health issues, because most public health specialists that I know (I helped train quite a few of them) are focused on improving individual lifestyles (stop smoking, exercise more, drink less). In this context, they may also target societal changes (such as the highly successful tobacco control programmes), but mainly with the aim of influencing individual behaviour. There appears to be little interest or expertise in general environmental influences on health (air pollution, pesticides and so on). There are exceptions to this – the local medical officers of health in Taranaki (Patrick O'Connor) and Bay of Plenty (Phil Shoemack) played important roles in their respective dioxin controversies.[50] Many other medical officers of health deal valiantly with such issues, usually with little or no help from MoH or their district health board, which simply don't have the expertise. The dilemmas faced by trained public health staff (health protection officers, public health nurses, public health medicine specialists) are aptly summarised by a colleague who has headed both the PHC and the Public Health Group in MoH:

They are trapped/targeted in two ways. Firstly, their generic line managers will bend over backwards not to upset their political masters ... Keeping in with that kind of culture helps to ensure that the mortgage continues to be paid. The second hierarchy is more insidious and even less transparent. There can be some people in that second hierarchy with very fixed beliefs who can have a subtle, negative impact on the careers of those public health practitioners who do not toe their line. Not rocking that particular boat helps to determine the size of the mortgage those practitioners can afford. Frustrated practitioners can either leak or leave![51]

Despite all the metamorphoses that occupational health and safety has gone through, no one seems to have mastered the skill of giving equal weight to health and safety (as the independent taskforce recommended).[52] Perhaps this is just too difficult – certainly, the skills and worldviews involved in these two areas are very different – and perhaps it was a mistake to move occupational health away from MoH in 1992. On the other hand, were it to move back there, or to a public health agency, mechanisms will be needed to ensure it receives appropriate attention.

The most striking problem is the lack of scientific expertise in the agencies dealing with occupational and environmental health. This problem was biggest with OSH, which quickly got rid of its medical and industrial hygiene expertise (or did not replace people when they left) so that after ten years all the expertise transferred from MoH had been lost.

Moreover, the little expertise that does exist in the agencies is often of the wrong type. Such agencies cannot cover everything, but they need a solid basis of scientific expertise, and the ability and willingness to collaborate with others who do have the relevant expertise. This is perhaps most apparent in the EPA NZ, where there appears to be little or no health expertise in general, and virtually none in epidemiology. Such expertise can only be attracted and retained through strong links with universities, with an emphasis on independence and creativeness, and with joint appointments, university academics being involved in specific committees and projects, and so on. As noted above, many overseas government agencies succeed in creating such environments, but they are rare in New Zealand – the PHC being a notable exception.

As Skegg notes, MoH and other government agencies are unwilling to make use of outside expertise ('it is almost as if the ministry has a morbid fear of such input').[53] I experienced the same thing on the National Health Committee, the Public Health Advisory Committee and the many other advisory committees I have served on. We were regarded as a necessary evil that had been imposed upon them and could easily be ignored. Similarly, DoL tended to regard the experts it inherited from MoH as being expensive and having 'inconvenient opinions'.

What, then, to do when an issue arises? First, you need to assemble scientists from the relevant fields for discussion and evaluation of the issue in an environment of mutual respect and communication. This is what the IARC does, although it gives (appropriately in my view) supremacy to the epidemiological data (the studies may not be perfect but at least we have the right species). Consensus can usually be reached, or at least the reasons for differing opinions can become clearer. Second, we must be willing to indicate that 'we don't really know – we think the risks are small, but we can't rule out the possibility that there is a risk'. This is rarely done in New Zealand, as shown by the EPA NZ's approach to glyphosate.

Even the best system in New Zealand will suffer from lack of expertise – we have great scientists but we are a small country. Thus, in general, it doesn't make sense for us to duplicate the work of international agencies such as the IARC. The toxicity of pesticides is similar around the world, so it makes no sense for us to go it alone. One gets the impression that this is in part done simply to bypass recommendations from the IARC and other agencies that are considered inconvenient. I am not saying New Zealand should accept all IARC decisions without question – US agencies occasionally question its decisions, and we have the same right. But rejecting or ignoring an IARC classification is a major event and should not be done by a few people behind the scenes in government departments. Rather, it requires a more public examination of the evidence by a highly qualified panel including overseas experts, with the reasons for disputing the classification made clear. This would only be needed in extremely rare circumstances.

So where does this leave us, and how relevant is the Covid-19 success story? What has been striking about Covid-19 is the arrogant unwillingness of European and North American governments and researchers to learn from successes in the rest of the world. Many

Asia-Pacific countries tackled the virus reasonably successfully because they had already had the experience of battling SARS, or they were countries such as New Zealand and Australia who were prepared to learn from their Asian neighbours. Strikingly, the Asia-Pacific experience got little mention in Europe and North America, except usually to say 'it wouldn't work for us'. If only US and UK governments and scientists had been prepared to learn from New Zealand's example, many many lives would have been saved.

The situation with environmental protection is largely the reverse. Just as arrogantly (or ironically, depending on your point of view), New Zealand keeps trying to go it alone in environmental protection, ignoring the advice and evidence from international agencies. If we had been prepared to learn from our colleagues overseas, our exposures to pesticides and the resulting health risks would have been greatly reduced. We don't need miracles; we just need to learn from 'best practice' overseas.

This does not mean that we should blindly accept what other countries are doing in terms of policy – what is an acceptable risk may be different for those in Washington DC, for example, and for iwi whose land and rivers are threatened. Aotearoa New Zealand needs to make its own decisions about policy, and what are acceptable risks. But first we have to review the evidence and know what the risks are – this is where we need to rely on international decisions and advice, rather than trying to go it alone.

There are many ways in which we can learn, but I would highlight two, which probably reflect my own interests and experience – I recognise that other things need to change too. Furthermore, I recognise that others may have better solutions, but here's what I think should happen.

First, I'm reluctant to recommend establishing a new agency – something done too often as a pseudo-solution in New Zealand – but in this case it is the least bad option. We are unlikely to achieve effective environmental protection without the (re)establishment of a dedicated and independent public health agency with its own legislation and budget, created as a Crown entity like other regulatory bodies in the public sector (for example, the EPA NZ), reporting annually to Parliament. In Skegg's book, he recognises that perhaps the PHC cannot be recreated in its previous form, though we need to learn from the experience.[54] However, something akin to it needs to be created – a public health agency working alongside MoH. MoH would then focus on treatment services but also have core public health expertise, particularly for policy purposes. Such an agency should also cover environmental and occupational health, including linkage to (or incorporation of) WorkSafe, as well as links to other relevant agencies such as the Ministry for the Environment. There are plenty of overseas models for this approach, such as the National Cancer Institute, the Centers for Disease Control and Prevention and the National Institute for Environmental Health Sciences in the US, and Public Health England in the UK. Any New Zealand model is likely to be different but can learn from all these.

Second, successful overseas models are not like classic government departments. Rather, they combine the best features of government departments and universities, with a strong focus on policy but also with strong independent research, involving the right mix of disciplines – and a willingness to collaborate across disciplines. The best ones involve many joint appointments, and people moving back and forth between the two settings. But mostly they have staff with the independence and integrity to tell the government news that it does not want to hear, to speak truth to power, and to the public – that's their job.

Appendix:
A Short Introduction to Dioxin

When the Ukrainian Security Service decided to poison Viktor Yushchenko (a Western-oriented candidate at a time when Ukraine was aligned with Russia) a few months before the December 2004 Ukrainian presidential election, it chose an unusual and remarkably inefficient method: dioxin. The day after Yushchenko had dinner with the service's chief, his wife noticed his breath smelled strange; the following day he consulted a doctor because of headache and stomach pain.

Several weeks later Yushchenko developed chloracne on his face – the acne-like rash that is the most distinctive feature of dioxin poisoning. In December 2004 an Amsterdam laboratory confirmed that he had a blood level of about 100,000 ppt, the second highest level ever recorded. A professor of environmental toxicology at the Free University in Amsterdam, Abraham Brouwer, reported that 'we don't actually know what the lethal dose is. The only thing we do know is that there's a woman who had an even higher dose, who didn't die, so it must be higher than that'. Yushchenko won the election and many years later is still alive, his chloracne having cleared up.

The term 'dioxin' actually refers to a whole group of chemicals, but is most commonly used to refer to 2,3,7,8-tetrachlorodibenzo-para-dioxin (TCDD), which is believed to be the most toxic form. However, there are about a dozen different types of dioxin, and a couple of them (see below) are just as toxic as TCDD.[1] Dioxin is a naturally occurring chemical that has been around for at least as long as fire has existed on Earth. You often hear arguments that things that are 'natural' (such as butter) are safer than things 'man-made' (such as margarine), but plenty of naturally occurring plants (hemlock, as in Socrates) and chemicals (arsenic, uranium and so on) are toxic, and dioxin is one of them. It is formed when chlorine-containing chemicals are burned.[2] Almost any fire will create some dioxin, particularly if it involves the burning of organic material in the presence of chlorine.

However, the background levels before the 1930s – such as those from natural and domestic fires – were very small compared with those resulting from industrial activities. Since then, large amounts of dioxin have been produced from car engines (particularly those using leaded petrol), production of iron and steel, metal processing and refining, and waste-burning incinerators. Dioxin is also created by the production of 'chlorinated aromatic chemicals' – the main source of dioxins in the environment. These include chlorine compounds from the chlorine bleaching of paper in pulp and paper mills; they also come from the production of polyvinyl chloride (PVC) plastics, some wood treatment chemicals (particularly PCP) and some pesticides.

Many different pesticides contain dioxins and dioxin-like compounds as contaminants, but attention has particularly focused on the phenoxy herbicides – some of which have been banned, but some of which are still being used. The best known are 2,4,5-T and 2,4-D. The phenoxy herbicides were introduced in 1946 and were widely used in agriculture in most Western countries by the 1950s. When they are sprayed on crops, such as wheat or corn, they kill the broadleaf plants (the weeds) by causing rapid uncontrolled growth, but leave 'grass family' crops (wheat, barley, rye, rice, corn) relatively unaffected. In New Zealand, however, they were mainly used for spraying woody weeds like gorse. In particular, 2,4,5-T was the main chemical used against gorse, and New Zealand's gorse problem meant that it became the highest per capita user of 2,4,5-T in the world.

The hazards of a chemical depend not only on its toxicity but also on the levels of exposure. For example, it is well established in animal studies that TCDD exposure in high doses can cause birth defects and cancer. Epidemiological studies of workers with very high exposures have also clearly demonstrated increased cancer risks. Accordingly, TCDD was classified as a proven human carcinogen by the WHO's IARC in 1997.[3] It has also been shown to cause reproductive and developmental effects in animals, including decreases in sperm counts, and birth defects.[4] So there is good reason for concern about intergenerational effects, such as birth defects in children of dioxin-exposed workers. What is still under debate is whether TCDD can cause detectable numbers of cancer cases or other health effects in workers with moderate levels of exposure, and/ or members of the general public with low exposure. The scientific debate, and the public controversy, has not been helped by the neglect of the issue by various

New Zealand government agencies, particularly in the 1980s, when the tendency was to dismiss the risks as 'trivial' or 'unproven'.

Abbreviations

2,4-D	2,4-dichlorophenoxyacetic acid
2,4,5-T	2,4,5-trichlorophenoxyacetic acid
CCA	copper-chrome-arsenate
CEC	Central Ethics Committee
DoL	Department of Labour
DSIR	Department of Scientific and Industrial Research
EFSA	European Food Safety Authority
EPA NZ	Environmental Protection Authority (New Zealand)
EPA US	Environmental Protection Agency (United States)
EPMU	Engineering, Printing and Manufacturing Union
ERMA	Environmental Risk Management Authority
ESR	Environmental Science and Research
EU	European Union
HRC	Health Research Council
HSNO Act	Hazardous Substances and New Organisms Act 1996 (NZ)
IARC	International Agency for Research on Cancer
IWD	Ivon Watkins-Dow
LSHTM	London School of Hygiene and Tropical Medicine
MoH	Ministry of Health
MUHEC	Massey University Human Ethics Committee
NIEHS	National Institute of Environmental Health Sciences
NIOEH	National Institute of Occupational and Environmental Health (Vietnam)
NOHSAC	National Occupational Safety and Health Advisory Committee
NTG	national task group
OSH	Occupational Safety and Health
PCDD	polychlorinated dibenzodioxin
PCDF	polychlorinated dibenzofuran
PCP	pentachlorophenol
pg/g	picograms per gram
PHC	Public Health Commission
ppm	parts per million
ppt	parts per trillion
SWAP	Sawmill Workers Against Poisons
TCDD	2,3,7,8-tetrachlorodibenzo-para-dioxin
TCP	2,4,5-trichlorophenol
WHO	World Health Organization

Notes

1 A Tale of Two Pandemics

1   EPA US, *Exposure and Human Health Reassessment of 2,3,7,8-Tetrachlorodibenzo-p-dioxin (TCDD) and Related Compounds: Part II – Health Assessment of 2,3,7,8-Tetrachlorodibenzo-p-dioxin (TCDD) and Related Compounds*, National Center for Environmental Assessment, Office of Research and Development, EPA US, Washington DC, 2000; M. Jacobs, 'The Role of the Ministry of Health', in H. Purnell, T. Slater, A. Eng and N. Pearce (eds), *Dioxin: Exposures, Health Effects and Public Policy, Proceedings of the 5th Annual CPHR Symposium in Health Research & Policy*, Centre for Public Health Research (CPHR), Wellington, 2006, pp.58–62.

2 Vietnam

1   A. Schecter et al., 'Agent Orange and the Vietnamese: The Persistence of Elevated Dioxin Levels in Human Tissues', *American Journal of Public Health*, 85, 4 (1995), pp.516–22, https://doi.org/10.2105/ajph.85.4.516 (accessed 15 March 2022).

2   Cathy Scott-Clark and Adrian Levy, 'Spectre Orange', *The Guardian*, 29 March 2003, www.theguardian.com/world/2003/mar/29/usa.adrianlevy (accessed 16 January 2022).

3   N. Pearce, 'Report on Visit to Vietnam as Part of US Delegation to Study the Health Effects of Agent Orange Exposure, 10-80 Committee to Study the Consequences of Chemicals Used during Wartime, Ho Chi Minh City', Wellington School of Medicine, Wellington, 1995.

4   R. Stone, 'Vietnam: Joint Dioxin Research Imperiled', *Science*, 269, 5222 (1995), p.298.

5   Robert Dreyfuss, 'Apocalypse Still', *Mother Jones*, January/February 2000, www.motherjones.com/politics/2000/01/apocalypse-still (accessed 16 January 2022).

6   National Academies of Sciences, Engineering, and Medicine, *Veterans and Agent Orange: Update 11*, The National Academies Press, Washington DC, 2018.

7   Ibid.

8   IARC Working Group on the Evaluation of Carcinogenic Risks to Humans, *IARC Monographs on the Evaluation of Carcinogenic Risks to Humans: Volume 69 – Polychlorinated Dibenzo-Para-Dioxins and Polychlorinated Dibenzofurans*, IARC, Lyon, 1997.

9   Advisory Committee on the Health of Veterans' Children, *Inquiry into the Health Status of Children of Vietnam and Operation Grapple Veterans*, Department of the Prime Minister and Cabinet, Wellington, June 1999.

10 Ibid.

11 Deborah McLeod, Donna Cormack and Tai Kake, *The Health Needs of the Children of Operation Grapple and Vietnam Veterans: A Critical Appraisal Undertaken for Veterans' Affairs, New Zealand Defence Force*, General Practice Department Report No. 4, New Zealand Defence Force, Wellington, August 2001.

12 Health Committee, *Inquiry into the Exposure of New Zealand Defence Personnel to Agent Orange and Other Defoliant Chemicals during the Vietnam War and Any Health Effects of That Exposure, and Transcripts of Evidence*, New Zealand House of Representatives, Wellington, October 2004.

13 Ibid., pp.24–27.

14 Helen Clark, 'Ministerial Statement to Parliament – Crown Apology to Viet Nam Veterans', New Zealand Government, 29 May 2008, www.beehive.govt.nz/release/ministerial-statement-parliament-crown-apology-viet-nam-veterans (accessed 16 January 2022).

3   Bringing It All Back Home

1   P. O'Connor, *Rates of Reported Illness in Paritutu and Moturoa*, Taranaki District Health Board, New Plymouth, 2001.

2   V. Baker, 'Science and Communities: ESR's Consultation Work with the Paritutu Community', in H. Purnell, T. Slater, A. Eng and N. Pearce (eds), *Dioxin: Exposures, Health Effects and Public Policy*, Proceedings of the 5th Annual CPHR Symposium in Health Research & Policy, CPHR, Wellington, 2006.

3   Ian Wishart and Simon Jones, 'Agent Orange: "We Buried It under New Plymouth"', *Investigate*, January/February 2001, pp.26–30, www.investigatemagazine.com/pdf's/jan2.pdf#Page=1 (accessed 17 January 2022).

4   V. Baker, J. Fowles, D. Phillips and N. Garrett, 'Appendix A: New Plymouth, Paritutu – Community Dioxin Exposure Assessment Study', in Jeff Fowles et al., *A Study of 2,3,7,8-Tetrachlorodibenzo-p-dioxin (TCDD) Exposures in Paritutu, New Zealand: Phase II – Serum Testing. An Interim Report to the New Zealand Ministry of Health*, ESR, Porirua, August 2004.

5   Ibid.
6   Ibid.
7   Ibid.
8   Ibid., p.4.
9   Ibid.
10 Wishart and Jones, 'Agent Orange'.
11 Robin Martin, '$3m Bill to Clean Dioxin Out of New Plymouth
    Wastewater Treatment Plant', Stuff, 15 February 2022, www.
    stuff.co.nz/national/rnz/300517951/3m-bill-to-clean-dioxin-
    out-of-new-plymouth-wastewater-treatment-plant (accessed
    15 March 2022).
12 O'Connor, Rates of Reported Illness in Paritutu and Moturoa.
13 G.L. Brinkman, R.E.F. Matthews and W.B. Earl, Possible Health
    Effects of Manufacture of 2,4,5-T in New Plymouth: Report of
    Ministerial Committee of Inquiry to the Minister of Health,
    Department of Health, Wellington, October 1986.
14 Ibid.
15 M. McNicholas, 'Look Back in Anguish', New Zealand Listener,
    2 October 2004, pp.26–27.
16 Baker, 'Science and Communities'.
17 O'Connor, Rates of Reported Illness in Paritutu and Moturoa.
18 Kevin Taylor, 'Report Set to Reverse Years of Denials on 2,4,5-T
    Danger', New Zealand Herald, 9 September 2004, www.nzherald.
    co.nz/nz/report-set-to-reverse-years-of-denials-on-245-t-danger/
    USW7LA36W7JE3LB3LLVA7QSUNY (accessed 17 January 2022).
19 O'Connor, Rates of Reported Illness in Paritutu and Moturoa.
20 Deborah Read and Craig Wright, Cancer Incidence and Mortality
    in New Plymouth, MoH, Wellington, October 2005.
21 B. Brockie, 'Well, It Might Give You Acne', Dominion Post,
    13 November 2006; A. Gibbs, 'Birth Defects Are a Real Legacy of
    Dioxin Poisoning', Dominion Post, 17 November 2006.
22 S. Catherall, 'First Blood as Officials Launch Dioxin Scare
    Inquiry', Sunday Star Times, 18 February 2001.
23 Jeff Fowles et al., A Study of 2,3,7,8-Tetrachlorodibenzo-p-dioxin
    (TCDD) Exposures in Paritutu, New Zealand: A Report to the
    New Zealand Ministry of Health, ESR, Porirua, 2005.
24 Jeff Fowles et al., A Study of 2,3,7,8-Tetrachlorodibenzo-p-dioxin
    (TCDD) Exposures in Paritutu, New Zealand: Phase II – Serum
    Testing. An Interim Report to the New Zealand Ministry of Health,
    ESR, Porirua, August 2004.
25 Taylor, 'Report Set to Reverse Years of Denials on 2,4,5-T Danger'.
26 S. Collins, '"Bizarre" Lack of Aid for Workers', New Zealand
    Herald, 11 September 2004.
27 Fowles et al., A Study of 2,3,7,8-Tetrachlorodibenzo-p-dioxin
    (TCDD) Exposures, 2005.

28   Ibid., p.iii.

29   Ibid.

30   H. Purnell, T. Slater, A. Eng and N. Pearce (eds), *Dioxin: Exposures, Health Effects and Public Policy*, Proceedings of the 5th Annual CPHR Symposium in Health Research & Policy, CPHR, Wellington, 2006.

31   P. Bertazzi, 'Health Effects of Environmental Exposures: The Case of Seveso', in Purnell et al. (eds), *Dioxin*; K. Steenland, 'Health Effects of Occupational Exposures: The Dioxin Wars and the Curious World of Risk Assessment', in Purnell et al. (eds), *Dioxin*; A.H. Smith, 'Public Health Policy and Dioxin in the Environment', in Purnell et al. (eds), *Dioxin*.

32   John Leonard, *TCDD Exposures in Paritutu New Plymouth*, Gerry Rea Associates, Auckland, 2006.

33   Broadcasting Standards Authority, 'Ministry of Health and CanWest TVWorks Ltd', BSA Decision No. 2007-012, 5 August 2009, www.bsa.govt.nz/decisions/all-decisions/ministry-of-health-and-canwest-tvworks-ltd-2007-012 (accessed 15 March 2022).

34   M. Jacobs, 'The Role of the Ministry of Health', in Purnell et al. (eds), *Dioxin*.

35   M. Kogevinas et al., 'Cancer Mortality in Workers Exposed to Phenoxy Herbicides, Chlorophenols, and Dioxins: An Expanded and Updated International Cohort Study', *American Journal of Epidemiology*, 145, 12 (1997), pp.1061–75, https://doi.org/10.1093/oxfordjournals.aje.a009069 (accessed 17 January 2022); R. Saracci et al., 'Cancer Mortality in Workers Exposed to Chlorophenoxy Herbicides and Chlorophenols', *The Lancet*, 338, 8774 (1991), pp.1027–32, https://doi.org/10.1016/0140-6736(91)91898-5 (accessed 17 January 2022); A. 't Mannetje, D. McLean, S. Cheng, P. Boffetta, D. Colin and N. Pearce, 'Mortality in New Zealand Workers Exposed to Phenoxy Herbicides and Dioxins', *Occupational and Environmental Medicine*, 62, 1 (2005), pp.34–40, https://doi.org/10.1136/oem.2004.015776 (accessed 17 January 2022).

36   Harvey Checkoway, Neil E. Pearce and David Kriebel, *Research Methods in Occupational Epidemiology*, 2nd edn, Oxford University Press, New York, 2004.

37   Kogevinas et al., 'Cancer Mortality in Workers Exposed to Phenoxy Herbicides, Chlorophenols, and Dioxins'; Saracci et al., 'Cancer Mortality in Workers Exposed to Chlorophenoxy Herbicides and Chlorophenols'.

38   Steenland, 'Health Effects of Occupational Exposures'.

39   't Mannetje et al., 'Mortality in New Zealand Workers Exposed to Phenoxy Herbicides and Dioxins'.

40   EPA US, *Exposure and Human Health Reassessment of 2,3,7,8-Tetrachlorodibenzo-p-dioxin (TCDD) and Related Compounds: Part II – Health Assessment of 2,3,7,8-Tetrachlorodibenzo-p-dioxin (TCDD) and Related Compounds*, National Center for Environmental Assessment, Office of Research and Development, EPA US, Washington DC, 2000.

41   Read and Wright, *Cancer Incidence and Mortality in New Plymouth*.

42   Fowles et al., *A Study of 2,3,7,8-Tetrachlorodibenzo-p-dioxin (TCDD) Exposures*, 2005; Kogevinas et al., 'Cancer Mortality in Workers Exposed to Phenoxy Herbicides, Chlorophenols, and Dioxins'; Saracci et al., 'Cancer Mortality in Workers Exposed to Chlorophenoxy Herbicides and Chlorophenols'; Fowles et al., *A Study of 2,3,7,8-Tetrachlorodibenzo-p-dioxin (TCDD) Exposures: Phase II*, 2004.

43   Dow AgroSciences and University of Otago, 'Otago Study Provides Assurance for Former 2,4,5-T Workers', press release, University of Otago, Dunedin, 13 March 2006.

44   Andrew Moore et al., *Review of the Current Processes for Ethical Review of Health and Disability Research in New Zealand: Report to the Minister of Health*, National Advisory Committee on Health and Disability Support Services Ethics, Wellington, May 2004.

45   A. 't Mannetje et al., 'Morbidity in New Zealand Pesticide Producers Exposed to 2,3,7,8-tetrachlorodibenzo-p-dioxin (TCDD)', *Environment International*, 110 (2018), pp.22–31, https://doi.org/10.1016/j.envint.2017.09.018 (accessed 17 January 2022).

46   P. Mocarelli et al., 'Paternal Concentrations of Dioxin and Sex Ratio of Offspring', *The Lancet*, 355, 9218 (2000), pp.1858–63, https://doi.org/10.1016/s0140-6736(00)02290-x (accessed 17 January 2022); Metrecia L. Terrell, Kathleen P. Hartnett and Michele Marcus, 'Can Environmental or Occupational Hazards Alter the Sex Ratio at Birth? A Systematic Review', *Emerging Health Threats Journal*, 4 (2011), 7109, https://doi.org/10.3402/ehtj.v4i0.7109 (accessed 17 January 2022).

47   IARC Working Group on the Evaluation of Carcinogenic Risks to Humans, *IARC Monographs on the Evaluation of Carcinogenic Risks to Humans: Volume 69 – Polychlorinated Dibenzo-Para-Dioxins and Polychlorinated Dibenzofurans*, IARC, Lyon, 1997.

4   Trouble at Mill

1   IARC Working Group on the Evaluation of Carcinogenic Risks to Humans, *IARC Monographs on the Evaluation of Carcinogenic*

Risks to Humans: Volume 117 – Pentachlorophenol and Some
Related Compounds, IARC, Lyon, 2019.

2   D. McLean et al., 'Morbidity in Former Sawmill Workers
Exposed to Pentachlorophenol (PCP): A Cross-Sectional Study
in New Zealand', American Journal of Industrial Medicine, 52, 4
(2009), pp.271–81, https://doi.org/10.1002/ajim.20677 (accessed
17 January 2022).

3   N. Bandaranayake et al., PCP in the Timber Industry: A Follow-Up of
Exposed Workers, Wellington School of Medicine, Wellington, 1999.

4   Ibid.

5   Ibid.

6   D. McLean and N. Pearce, Final Report on the Feasibility of
Research into the Mortality, Cancer Incidence and Morbidity
Experience of New Zealand Timber Workers Who Worked with
PCP, CPHR, Wellington, 2002.

7   D. McLean, 'Mortality and Morbidity Studies of Former Timber
Workers', in H. Purnell, T. Slater, A. Eng and N. Pearce (eds),
Dioxin: Exposures, Health Effects and Public Policy, Proceedings
of the 5th Annual CPHR Symposium in Health Research & Policy,
CPHR, Wellington, 2006.

8   H. Purnell, T. Slater, A. Eng and N. Pearce (eds), Dioxin:
Exposures, Health Effects and Public Policy, Proceedings of the
5th Annual CPHR Symposium in Health Research & Policy,
CPHR, Wellington, 2006.

9   K. Dew, 'National Identity and Controversy: New Zealand's Clean
Green Image and Pentachlorophenol', Health and Place, 5, 1
(1999), pp.45–57, https://doi.org/10.1016/s1353-8292(98)00040-9
(accessed 15 March 2022).

10   Bandaranayake et al., PCP in the Timber Industry.

11   New Zealand National Task Group on Site Contamination from
the Use of Timber Treatment Chemicals, Pentachlorophenol
Risk Assessment Pilot Study: National Task Group Study Team
Report, Ministry for the Environment and Department of Health,
Wellington, July 1992.

12   Bandaranayake et al., PCP in the Timber Industry.

13   Dew, 'National Identity and Controversy'.

14   Bandaranayake et al., PCP in the Timber Industry.

15   Ibid.

16   Ibid.

17   Ibid.

18   K.Z. Guyton et al., 'Carcinogenicity of Pentachlorophenol and
Some Related Compounds', The Lancet Oncology, 17, 12 (2016),
pp.1637–38, https://doi.org/10.1016/s1470-2045(16)30513-7
(accessed 17 January 2022).

19   Bandaranayake et al., PCP in the Timber Industry.

20   Dew, 'National Identity and Controversy'.
21   Ibid.
22   R. Middlemiss, 'Community Responses', in Purnell et al. (eds), *Dioxin*.
23   Ibid.
24   Bandaranayake et al., *PCP in the Timber Industry*.
25   A.H. Smith and P. Lopipero, *Evaluation of the Toxicity of Dioxins and Dioxin-Like PCBs: A Health Risk Appraisal for the New Zealand Population. A Report to the Ministry for the Environment*, Ministry for the Environment, Wellington, February 2001.
26   C.B. Walls, W.I. Glass and N.E. Pearce, 'Health Effects of Occupational Pentachlorophenol Exposure in Timber Sawmill Employees: A Preliminary Study', *New Zealand Medical Journal*, 111, 1074 (1998), pp.362–64.
27   D. McLean et al., 'Serum Dioxin Levels in Former New Zealand Sawmill Workers Twenty Years after Exposure to Pentachlorophenol (PCP) Ceased', *Chemosphere*, 74, 7 (2009), pp.962–67, https://doi.org/10.1016/j.chemosphere.2008.10.017 (accessed 17 January 2022).
28   McLean et al., 'Morbidity in Former Sawmill Workers Exposed to Pentachlorophenol (PCP)'.

5   Where Are We Now?

1   V. Baker, 'Science and Communities: ESR's Consultation Work with the Paritutu Community', in H. Purnell, T. Slater, A. Eng and N. Pearce (eds), *Dioxin: Exposures, Health Effects and Public Policy*, Proceedings of the 5th Annual CPHR Symposium in Health Research & Policy, CPHR, Wellington, 2006.
2   A. 't Mannetje, 'The Carcinogenicity of Pesticides Used in New Zealand', *New Zealand Medical Journal*, 133, 1526 (2020), pp.76–88.
3   D. Manktelow et al., *Trends in Pesticide Use in New Zealand: 2004*, Ministry for the Environment, Wellington, November 2005.
4   A. Eng et al., 'The New Zealand Workforce Survey I: Self-Reported Occupational Exposures', *Annals of Occupational Hygiene*, 54, 2 (2010), pp.144–53, https://doi.org/10.1093/annhyg/mep097 (accessed 17 January 2022).
5   A. 't Mannetje and N. Pearce, 'Quantitative Estimates of Work-Related Death, Disease and Injury in New Zealand', *Scandinavian Journal of Work, Environment & Health*, 31, 4 (2005), pp.266–76, https://doi.org/10.5271/sjweh.882 (accessed 17 January 2022).
6   G. Chen, J. Douwes, J. van den Berg, N. Pearce, H. Kromhout, B. Glass, D. McLean and A. 't Mannetje, 'Occupational Exposures to

Pesticides and Other Chemicals: A New Zealand Motor Neuron Disease Case-Control Study', *Occupational and Environmental Medicine* (2022), https://doi.org/10.1136/oemed-2021-108056 (accessed 9 May 2022).

7   Sam Wong, 'Strongest Evidence Yet that Neonicotinoids Are Killing Bees', *New Scientist*, 3 July 2017, www.newscientist.com/article/2139197-strongest-evidence-yet-that-neonicotinoids-are-killing-bees (accessed 17 January 2022).

8   Phil Pennington, 'Another 75,000 Tonnes of Toxic Waste Revealed to Be Stored Near Beach at Tiwai Point', Radio New Zealand, 8 March 2021, www.rnz.co.nz/news/national/437867/another-75-000-tonnes-of-toxic-waste-revealed-to-be-stored-near-beach-at-tiwai-point (accessed 17 January 2022); 'Company at Top of Dumping Breach List Takes on Big New Contract', Radio New Zealand, 25 February 2021, www.rnz.co.nz/news/in-depth/437130/company-at-top-of-dumping-breach-list-takes-on-big-new-contract (accessed 17 January 2022); Conan Young, 'Nitrates in Canterbury River Up 50 Per Cent in 22 Months, Fishing Group Says', Stuff, 10 May 2021, www.stuff.co.nz/environment/125082037/nitrates-in-canterbury-river-up-50-per-cent-in-22-months-fishing-group-says (accessed 17 January 2022); Charlie O'Mannin, 'Intensive Farming in Mackenzie Damaging Native Species, Report Says', *Timaru Herald*, 18 April 2021, www.stuff.co.nz/timaru-herald/news/300279596/intensive-farming-in-mackenzie-damaging-native-species-report-says (accessed 17 January 2022).

9   Nick Stringer, 'Glyphosate Is Farming's Favourite Weed Killer. Can NZ Learn to Live Without It?' The Spinoff, 1 June 2021, https://thespinoff.co.nz/business/01-06-2021/glyphosate-is-farmings-favourite-weed-killer-can-nz-learn-to-live-without-it (accessed 17 January 2022); Jan Wright, *Evaluating the Use of 1080: Predators, Poisons and Silent Forests*, Parliamentary Commissioner for the Environment, Wellington, June 2011.

10   Andy Brew, 'Toxic Timber Filling Up New Zealand's Landfills', *New Zealand Herald*, 10 June 2021, www.nzherald.co.nz/nz/toxic-timber-filling-up-new-zealands-landfills/PHRNERUQW25JVZ7RCSW5JFE6OA (accessed 17 January 2022).

11   N.E. Pearce, R.A. Sheppard, A.H. Smith and C.A. Teague, 'Non-Hodgkin's Lymphoma and Farming: An Expanded Case-Control Study', *International Journal of Cancer*, 39, 2 (1987), pp.155–61, https://doi.org/10.1002/ijc.2910390206 (accessed 17 January 2022); N.E. Pearce, A.H. Smith, J.K. Howard, R.A. Sheppard, H.J. Giles and C.A. Teague, 'Non-Hodgkin's

Lymphoma and Exposure to Phenoxyherbicides, Chlorophenols, Fencing Work, and Meat Works Employment: A Case-Control Study', *British Journal of Industrial Medicine*, 43, 2 (1986), pp.75–83, https://doi.org/10.1136%2Foem.43.2.75 (accessed 17 January 2022).

12   'Kopeopeo Canal Remediation – Monitoring Phase', Bay of Plenty Regional Council, www.boprc.govt.nz/our-projects/kopeopeo-canal-remediation-monitoring-phase (accessed 17 January 2022).

13   R. Beasley et al., 'Asbestos Related Medical Disorders and the New Zealand Asbestos Disease Register', Therapeutic Notes No. 212, Department of Health, Wellington, 1991.

14   J. Douwes, A. 't Mannetje, D. McLean, N. Pearce, A. Woodward and J.D. Potter, 'Carcinogenicity of Glyphosate: Why Is New Zealand's EPA Lost in the Weeds?' *New Zealand Medical Journal*, 131, 1472 (2018), pp.82–89.

15   K.Z. Guyton et al., 'Carcinogenicity of Tetrachlorvinphos, Parathion, Malathion, Diazinon, and Glyphosate', *The Lancet Oncology*, 16, 5 (2015), pp.490–91, https://doi.org/10.1016/s1470-2045(15)70134-8 (accessed 17 January 2022); Manolis Kogevinas, 'Probable Carcinogenicity of Glyphosate', *British Medical Journal*, 365, (2019), l1613, https://doi.org/10.1136/bmj.l1613 (accessed 17 January 2022).

16   J.M. Samet et al., 'The IARC Monographs: Updated Procedures for Modern and Transparent Evidence Synthesis in Cancer Hazard Identification', *Journal of the National Cancer Institute*, 112, 1 (2020), pp.30–37, https://doi.org/10.1093/jnci/djz169 (accessed 18 January 2022).

17   N. Pearce, 'Review of: Kabat GC. Hyping Health Risks: Environmental Hazards in Daily Life and the Science of Epidemiology', *International Journal of Epidemiology*, 38 (2009), pp.1746–49.

18   N. Pearce et al., 'IARC Monographs: 40 Years of Evaluating Carcinogenic Hazards to Humans', *Environmental Health Perspectives*, 123, 6 (2015), pp.507–14, https://doi.org/10.1289/ehp.1409149 (accessed 17 January 2022).

19   Kai Kupferschmidt, 'High-Profile Cancer Reviews Trigger Controversy', *Science*, 352, 6293 (2016), pp.1504–5, https://doi.org/10.1126/science.352.6293.1504 (accessed 18 January 2022).

20   David Michaels, 'Doubt Is Their Product', *Scientific American*, 292, 6 (2005), pp.96–101, www.scientificamerican.com/article/doubt-is-their-product (accessed 18 January 2022); David Michaels, 'Manufactured Uncertainty: Protecting Public Health in the Age of Contested Science and Product Defense', *Annals of the New York Academy of Sciences*, 1076 (2006),

pp.149–62, https://doi.org/10.1196/annals.1371.058 (accessed 18 January 2022).

21   Neil Pearce, 'Independent, Rigorous, Vilified – Why Attacks on the International Agency for Research on Cancer Are Unfair', London School of Hygiene & Tropical Medicine, 15 August 2018, www.lshtm.ac.uk/newsevents/expert-opinion/independent-rigorous-vilified-why-attacks-international-agency-research (accessed 18 January 2022).

22   Geoffrey Kabat, 'Claims that Criticism of IARC Are Industry-Driven Do IARC More Harm than Good', American Council on Science and Health, 23 August 2018, www.acsh.org/news/2018/08/23/claims-criticism-iarc-are-industry-driven-do-iarc-more-harm-good-13350 (accessed 18 January 2022).

23   N. Pearce, *Adverse Reactions: The Fenoterol Story*, Auckland University Press, 2007; Pearce, 'Review of: Kabat GC. Hyping Health Risks'; N. Pearce, 'Adverse Reactions: The Fenoterol Saga', in P. Davis (ed.), *For Health or Profit: The Pharmaceutical Industry in New Zealand*, Oxford University Press, Auckland, 1992, pp.75–97; N. Pearce, 'Adverse Reactions, Social Responses: A Tale of Two Asthma Mortality Epidemics', in P. Davis (ed.), *Contested Ground: Public Purpose and Private Interest in the Regulation of Prescription Drugs*, Oxford University Press, New York, 1996, pp.57–75; N. Pearce, 'Public Health and the Precautionary Principle', in Marco Martuzzi and Joel A. Tickner (eds), *The Precautionary Principle: Protecting Public Health, the Environment, and the Future of Our Children*, WHO Regional Office for Europe, Rome, 2004, pp.49–62; N. Pearce, 'The Rise and Rise of Corporate Epidemiology and the Narrowing of Epidemiology's Vision', *International Journal of Epidemiology*, 36 (2007), pp.713–17; N. Pearce, 'Corporate Influences on Epidemiology', *International Journal of Epidemiology*, 37, 1 (2008), pp.46–53, https://doi.org/10.1093/ije/dym270 (accessed 18 January 2022); N. Pearce, 'Response: The Distribution and Determinants of Epidemiologic Research', *International Journal of Epidemiology*, 37, 1 (2008), pp.65–68, https://doi.org/10.1093/ije/dym268 (accessed 19 January 2022).

24   N. Pearce and J.P. Vandenbroucke, 'Arguments about Face Masks and Covid-19 Reflect Broader Methodologic Debates within Medical Science', *European Journal of Epidemiology*, 36, 2 (2021), pp.143–47, https://doi.org/10.1007/s10654-021-00735-7 (accessed 18 January 2022).

25   European Food Safety Authority, 'Conclusion on the Peer Review of the Pesticide Risk Assessment of the Active Substance Glyphosate', *EFSA Journal*, 13, 11 (2015), 4302, https://doi.org/10.2903/j.efsa.2015.4302 (accessed 18 January 2022).

26   C.J. Portier et al., 'Differences in the Carcinogenic Evaluation of Glyphosate between the International Agency for Research on Cancer (IARC) and the European Food Safety Authority (EFSA)', *Journal of Epidemiology and Community Health*, 70, 8 (2016), pp.741–45, https://doi.org/10.1136/jech-2015-207005 (accessed 18 January 2022).

27   Douwes et al., 'Carcinogenicity of Glyphosate'; Arthur Neslen, 'EU Report on Weedkiller Safety Copied Text from Monsanto Study', *The Guardian*, 15 September 2015, www.theguardian.com/environment/22017/sep/15/eu-report-on-weedkiller-safety-copied-text-from-monsanto-study (accessed 18 January 2022).

28   S. More et al., 'Draft for Internal Testing Scientific Committee Guidance on Appraising and Integrating Evidence from Epidemiological Studies for Use in EFSA's Scientific Assessments', *EFSA Journal*, 18, 8 (2020), e06221, https://doi.org/10.2903%2Fj.efsa.2020.6221 (accessed 18 January 2022).

29   Carey Gillam, 'Corporate Studies Asserting Herbicide Safety Show Many Flaws, New Analysis Finds', *The Guardian*, 2 July 2021, www.theguardian.com/business/2021/jul/02/glyphosate-herbicide-roundup-corporate-safety-studies (accessed 18 January 2022).

30   W. Temple, *Review of the Evidence Relating to Glyphosate and Carcinogenicity*, EPA NZ, Wellington, August 2016, www.epa.govt.nz/assets/Uploads/Documents/Everyday-Environment/Publications/EPA-glyphosate-review.pdf (accessed 18 January 2022); Douwes et al., 'Carcinogenicity of Glyphosate'.

31   J.I. Bruning and S. Browning, *Public Health Concern: Why Did the NZ EPA Ignore the World Authority on Cancer?*, Green Party of Aotearoa New Zealand, Wellington, August 2017, https://atlas.boprc.govt.nz/api/v1/edms/document/A2773595/content (accessed 18 January 2022).

32   Kate Kelland, 'Cancer Agency Left in the Dark over Glyphosate Evidence', Reuters Investigates, 14 June 2017, www.reuters.com/investigates/special-report/glyphosate-cancer-data (accessed 18 January 2022); J. Rowarth, 'Regulators Heed Facts Despite Public Fear of Herbicide', *National Business Review*, 7 July 2017, www.nbr.co.nz/opinion/regulators-heed-facts-despite-public-fear-herbicide (accessed 18 January 2022).

33   Douwes et al., 'Carcinogenicity of Glyphosate'; K. Kelland, 'Midday Rural News', Radio New Zealand, 31 July 2017, www.rnz.co.nz/audio/player?audio_id=201852997 (accessed 18 January 2022).

34   Stringer, 'Glyphosate Is Farming's Favourite Weed Killer'.

35   'Dioxins: Frequently Asked Questions', Ministry for the Environment, 2016.

36 't Mannetje, 'The Carcinogenicity of Pesticides Used in New Zealand'.

37 Pearce et al., 'Non-Hodgkin's Lymphoma and Farming'; N. Pearce and M. Porta, 'Association of Non-Hodgkin's Lymphoma with Rheumatoid Arthritis', *American Journal of Medicine*, 81, 4 (1986), pp.747–48, https://doi.org/10.1016/0002-9343(86)-90573-5 (accessed 18 January 2022).

38 A. 't Mannetje et al., 'High Risk Occupations for Non-Hodgkin's Lymphoma in New Zealand: Case-Control Study', *Occupational and Environmental Medicine*, 65, 5 (2008), pp.354–63, https://doi.org/10.1136/oem.2007.035014 (accessed 18 January 2022).

39 D. Loomis et al., 'Carcinogenicity of Lindane, DDT, and 2,4-Dichlorophenoxyacetic Acid', *The Lancet Oncology*, 16, 8 (2015), pp.891–92, https://doi.org/10.1016/s1470-2045(15)00081-9 (accessed 18 January 2022).

40 M. Kogevinas et al., 'Cancer Mortality in Workers Exposed to Phenoxy Herbicides, Chlorophenols, and Dioxins: An Expanded and Updated International Cohort Study', *American Journal of Epidemiology*, 145, 12 (1997), pp.1061–75, https://doi.org/10.1093/oxfordjournals.aje.a009069 (accessed 17 January 2022).

41 P. Hay, *Classification of Phenoxy Herbicides: Letter to ERMA*, Nufarm, Melbourne, 2003.

42 A. 't Mannetje, D. McLean, S. Cheng, P. Boffetta, D. Colin and N. Pearce, 'Mortality in New Zealand Workers Exposed to Phenoxy Herbicides and Dioxins', *Occupational and Environmental Medicine*, 62, 1 (2005), pp.34–40, https://doi.org/10.1136/oem.2004.015776 (accessed 17 January 2022).

43 Neil Pearce and Dave McLean, 'Agricultural Exposures and Non-Hodgkin's Lymphoma', *Scandinavian Journal of Work, Environment & Health*, 31, Supp. 1 (2005), pp.18–25, discussion 5–7.

6 So How Do We Fix It?

1 'Support Service for Dioxin Exposed People', Ministry of Health, www.health.govt.nz/our-work/environmental-health/dioxins/dioxins-health-support-services/support-service-dioxin-exposed-people (accessed 18 January 2022).

2 J. Tudor Hart, 'Commentary: Three Decades of the Inverse Care Law', *British Medical Journal*, 320, 7226 (2000), pp.18–19.

3 David Skegg, *The Health of the People*, Bridget Williams Books, Wellington, 2019.

4 M. McKee et al., 'Towards a Comprehensive Global Approach to Prevention and Control of NCDs', *Globalization and Health*, 10 (2014), 74, https://doi.org/10.1186%2Fs12992-014-0074-8

(accessed 18 January 2022); N. Pearce et al., 'Global Prevention and Control of NCDs: Limitations of the Standard Approach', *Journal of Public Health Policy*, 36, 4 (2015), pp.408–25, https://doi.org/10.1057/jphp.2015.29 (accessed 18 January 2022).

5   R. Saracci, 'Counterpoint: Epidemiology's Dual Social Commitment – Science and Health', *American Journal of Epidemiology*, 190, 6 (2021), pp.980–83.

6   N. Pearce, 'Why We Need a Ministry of Public Health', *PHA News*, 6.3 (2003), pp.1–2; N. Pearce, 'The Ideal Minister of (Public) Health', *Journal of Epidemiology and Community Health*, 56, 12 (2002), pp.888–89, https://doi.org/10.1136%2Fjech.56.12.888-a (accessed 18 January 2022).

7   Skegg, *The Health of the People*.

8   PHC, *Our Health, Our Future, Hauora Pakari, Koiora Roa: The State of the Public Health in New Zealand*, PHC, Wellington, 1993; PHC, *Our Health, Our Future, Hauora Pakari, Koiora Roa: The State of the Public Health in New Zealand*, PHC, Wellington, 1994.

9   PHC, *Healthy: The Newsletter of the Public Health Commission*, Issue 8, PHC, Wellington, June 1995.

10   Skegg, *The Health of the People*.

11   Ibid.; T.A. Krieble, 'The Rise and Fall of a Crown Entity: A Case Study of the Public Health Commission', Master's thesis, Victoria University of Wellington, 1996.

12   Skegg, *The Health of the People*.

13   L. Holloway et al., *Meeting the Needs of People with Chronic Conditions*, National Advisory Committee on Health and Disability, Wellington, 2007, www.health.govt.nz/system/files/documents/publications/meeting-needs-chronic-conditions-feb07.pdf (accessed 18 January 2022); Wairarapa Māori Executive/Taiwhenua o Ngati Kahungunu ki Wairarapa, *Te Reo o te Ora: The Wairarapa Māori Asthma Project*, Huia, Wellington, 1992; Wairarapa Māori Executive/Taiwhenua o Ngati Kahungunu ki Wairarapa, Te Hauora Runanga o Wairarapa, Wellington Clinical School of Medicine and Wellington Asthma Research Group, *Te Reo o te Ora: The Wairarapa Māori Asthma Project and the Six Year Follow-up*, 2nd edn, Huia, Wellington, 1999.

14   'Health System Reform: What the Experts Are Saying', Radio New Zealand, 22 April 2021, www.rnz.co.nz/news/national/440988/health-system-reform-what-the-experts-are-saying (accessed 19 January 2022).

15   G. Durham, personal communication, 2021.

16   N. Pearce, 'Who Cares about Occupational Health?' *PHA News*, 7.4 (2004), pp.4–5.

17   N. Pearce, D. McLean and R. Berry (eds), *Priorities in Occupational Health and Safety: Proceedings of the Second Annual CPHR Symposium in Health Research and Policy*, Occasional Report Series No. 3, CPHR, Wellington, July 2003.

18   N. Pearce, E. Dryson, A.-M. Feyer, P. Gander, S. McCracken and M. Wagstaffe, *The Burden of Occupational Disease and Injury in New Zealand: Report to the Associate Minister of Labour*, NOHSAC, Wellington, 2004; N. Pearce, E. Dryson, A.-M. Feyer, P. Gander, S. McCracken and M. Wagstaffe, *Surveillance of Occupational Disease and Injury in New Zealand: Report to the Minister of Labour*, NOHSAC, Wellington, 2005; N. Pearce, E. Dryson, A.-M. Feyer, P. Gander, S. McCracken and M. Wagstaffe, *Surveillance and Control of Workplace Exposures in New Zealand: Report to the Minister of Labour*, NOHSAC, Wellington, 2006; N. Pearce, E. Dryson, P. Gander, J. Langley and M. Wagstaffe, *National Profile of Occupational Health and Safety in New Zealand: Report to the Minister of Labour*, NOHSAC, Wellington, 2007.

19   Pearce et al., *The Burden of Occupational Disease and Injury in New Zealand*.

20   Pearce et al., *Surveillance of Occupational Disease and Injury in New Zealand*; Pearce et al., *Surveillance and Control of Workplace Exposures in New Zealand*; L. Pezzullo and A. Crook, *The Economic and Social Costs of Occupational Disease and Injury in New Zealand*, NOHSAC, Wellington, 2006; Pearce et al., *National Profile of Occupational Health and Safety in New Zealand*; N. Pearce, E. Dryson, P. Gander, J. Langley and M. Wagstaffe, *Review of the Key Characteristics that Determine the Efficacy of OHS Instruments: Report to the Minister of Labour*, NOHSAC, Wellington, 2008; P. Gander, N. Pearce, J. Langley and M. Wagstaffe, *The Evolving Work Environment in New Zealand: Implications for Occupational Health and Safety – Report to the Minister of Labour*, NOHSAC, Wellington, 2009; Allen and Clarke, *Defining Work-Related Harm: Implications for Diagnosis, Rehabilitation, Compensation and Prevention*, NOHSAC Technical Report No. 11, NOHSAC, Wellington, 2009; S. Legg et al., *Occupational Health and Safety in Small Businesses*, NOHSAC Technical Report No. 12, NOHSAC, Wellington, 2009; A. 't Mannetje, T. Slater, D. McLean, A. Eng, C. Briar and J. Douwes, *Women's Occupational Health and Safety in New Zealand*, NOHSAC Technical Report No. 13, NOHSAC, Wellington, 2009.

21   R. Jager, P. Rose, P. Mackay, B. Rosenberg, M. Mullins and M. Cosman, *Report of the Independent Taskforce on Workplace Health and Safety*, Independent Taskforce on Workplace Health and Safety, Wellington, 2013; Pearce et al., *National Profile of Occupational Health and Safety in New Zealand*.

22 A. Eng et al., 'The New Zealand Workforce Survey I: Self-Reported Occupational Exposures', *Annals of Occupational Hygiene*, 54, 2 (2010), pp.144–53, https://doi.org/10.1093/annhyg/mep097 (accessed 17 January 2022); A. Eng et al., 'The New Zealand Workforce Survey II: Occupational Risk Factors for Asthma', *Annals of Occupational Hygiene*, 54, 2 (2010), pp.154–64, https://doi.org/10.1093/annhyg/mep098 (accessed 19 January 2022); A. Eng, A. 't Mannetje, L. Ellison-Loschmann, D. McLean, S. Cheng and N. Pearce, 'Ethnic Differences in Patterns of Occupational Exposure in New Zealand', *American Journal of Industrial Medicine*, 54, 5 (2011), pp.410–18, https://doi.org/10.1002/ajim.20934 (accessed 19 January 2022); A. Eng, A. 't Mannetje, D. McLean, L. Ellison-Loschmann, S. Cheng and N. Pearce, 'Gender Differences in Occupational Exposure Patterns', *Occupational and Environmental Medicine*, 68, 12 (2011), pp.888–94, https://doi.org/10.1136/oem.2010.064097 (accessed 19 January 2022).

23 M. Bates and J. Fowles, *Proposal for the Development of a National Surveillance System for Injuries Caused by Hazardous Substances: Discussion Document Prepared for the New Zealand Ministry of Health*, ESR, Porirua, May 2000.

24 J. Fowles, *The Notification of Injuries from Hazardous Substances: Guidelines and Reference Material for the Public Services*, ESR, Porirua, 2001.

25 J. Douwes, A. 't Mannetje, D. McLean, N. Pearce, A. Woodward and J.D. Potter, 'Carcinogenicity of Glyphosate: Why Is New Zealand's EPA Lost in the Weeds?' *New Zealand Medical Journal*, 131, 1472 (2018), pp.82–89.

26 IARC Working Group on the Evaluation of Carcinogenic Risks to Humans, *IARC Monographs on the Evaluation of Carcinogenic Risks to Humans: Volume 100C – Arsenic, Metals, Fibres and Dusts*, IARC, Lyon, 2012.

27 N. Pearce and J.P. Vandenbroucke, 'Arguments about Face Masks and Covid-19 Reflect Broader Methodologic Debates within Medical Science', *European Journal of Epidemiology*, 36, 2 (2021), pp.143–47, https://doi.org/10.1007/s10654-021-00735-7 (accessed 18 January 2022).

28 G.H. Guyatt et al., 'GRADE Guidelines: 4. Rating the Quality of Evidence-Study Limitations (Risk of Bias)', *Journal of Clinical Epidemiology*, 64, 4 (2011), pp.407–15, https://doi.org/10.1016/j.jclinepi.2010.07.017 (accessed 19 January 2022); J.A. Sterne et al., 'ROBINS-I: A Tool for Assessing Risk of Bias in Non-Randomised Studies of Interventions', *British Medical Journal*, 355 (2016), i4919, https://doi.org/10.1136/bmj.i4919 (accessed 19 January 2022).

29   K. Steenland et al., 'Risk of Bias Assessments and Evidence
     Syntheses for Observational Epidemiologic Studies of
     Environmental and Occupational Exposures: Strengths
     and Limitations', *Environmental Health Perspectives*, 128, 9
     (2020), 95002, https://doi.org/10.1289/EHP6980 (accessed
     19 January 2022); R.W.M. Vernooij et al., 'Patterns of Red and
     Processed Meat Consumption and Risk for Cardiometabolic
     and Cancer Outcomes: A Systematic Review and Meta-Analysis
     of Cohort Studies', *Annals of Internal Medicine*, 171, 10 (2019),
     pp.732–41, https://doi.org/10.7326/m19-1583 (accessed
     19 January 2022).

30   D.A. Lawlor, K. Tilling and G. Davey Smith, 'Triangulation
     in Aetiological Epidemiology', *International Journal of
     Epidemiology*, 45, 6 (2016), pp.1866–86, https://doi.org/10.1093/
     ije/dyw314 (accessed 19 January 2022); A. Broadbent,
     J.P. Vandenbroucke and N. Pearce, 'Formalism or Pluralism?
     A Reply to Commentaries on "Causality and Causal Inference
     in Epidemiology"', *International Journal of Epidemiology*, 45, 6
     (2016), pp.1841–51, https://doi.org/10.1093/ije/dyw298 (accessed
     18 January 2022); J. Vandenbroucke, A. Broadbent and N. Pearce,
     'Causality and Causal Inference in Epidemiology – The Need for
     a Pluralistic Approach', *International Journal of Epidemiology*,
     45, 6 (2016), pp.1776–86, https://doi.org/10.1093/ije/dyv341
     (accessed 19 January 2022).

31   N. Pearce, 'Review of: Kabat GC. Hyping Health Risks:
     Environmental Hazards in Daily Life and the Science of
     Epidemiology', *International Journal of Epidemiology*, 38 (2009),
     pp.1746–49; N. Pearce, 'Corporate Influences on Epidemiology',
     International Journal of Epidemiology, 37, 1 (2008), pp.46–53,
     https://doi.org/10.1093/ije/dym270 (accessed 18 January 2022);
     N. Pearce, 'Response: The Distribution and Determinants of
     Epidemiologic Research', *International Journal of Epidemiology*,
     37, 1 (2008), pp.65–68, https://doi.org/10.1093/ije/dym268
     (accessed 19 January 2022); N. Oreskes and E.M. Conway,
     *Merchants of Doubt: How a Handful of Scientists Obscured the
     Truth on Issues from Tobacco Smoking to Global Warming*,
     Bloomsbury Press, New York, 2011.

32   N. Pearce, 'Public Health and the Precautionary Principle', in
     Marco Martuzzi and Joel A. Tickner (eds), *The Precautionary
     Principle: Protecting Public Health, the Environment and the
     Future of Our Children*, WHO Regional Office for Europe, Rome,
     2004, pp.49–62.

33   IWD, *Don't Cry Wolf about 2,4,5-T When There Isn't One*, IWD,
     New Plymouth, 1980.

34   B.F. Cain (ed.), *Assessment of Toxic Hazards of the Herbicide*

2,4,5-T in New Zealand: Synopsis of Presentations Made to the
Royal Society of New Zealand on the Occasion of the Fellows'
Annual Meeting 21 May 1980, Royal Society of New Zealand,
Wellington, 1980.

35   Ibid., p.14.

36   Ibid., p.10.

37   J. Stoke, Health Effects of the Manufacture and Use of 2,4,5-T,
MoH, Wellington, 1985.

38   D. Read, 'The Science-Public Interface: Paritutu Serum Dioxin
Study', in H. Purnell, T. Slater, A. Eng and N. Pearce (eds), Dioxin:
Exposures, Health Effects and Public Policy, Proceedings of the
5th Annual CPHR Symposium in Health Research & Policy,
CPHR, Wellington, 2006.

39   G.L. Brinkman, R.E.F. Matthews and W.B. Earl, Possible Health
Effects of Manufacture of 2,4,5-T in New Plymouth: Report of
Ministerial Committee of Inquiry to the Minister of Health,
Department of Health, Wellington, October 1986.

40   P. Bensemann, 'Watchdog Vote Halves 245T Tests', The Dominion,
12 August 1986.

41   P. Bensemann, 'Health Officials Deny 245T Bias', The Dominion,
7 August 1986; P. Bensemann, '245T Report Criticises Officials',
The Dominion, 6 August 1986.

42   'Inquiry into 2,4,5-T Hears of Tragedies', Evening Post, 6 August
1986.

43   R. Saracci et al., 'Cancer Mortality in Workers Exposed
to Chlorophenoxy Herbicides and Chlorophenols',
The Lancet, 338, 8774 (1991), pp.1027–32, https://doi.
org/10.1016/0140-6736(91)91898-5 (accessed 17 January 2022);
IARC Working Group on the Evaluation of Carcinogenic Risks
to Humans, IARC Monographs on the Evaluation of Carcinogenic
Risks to Humans: Volume 69 – Polychlorinated Dibenzo-
Para-Dioxins and Polychlorinated Dibenzofurans, IARC, Lyon,
1997.

44   G. Paul and J. Harawira, 'Community Responses', in H. Purnell,
T. Slater, A. Eng and N. Pearce (eds), Dioxin: Exposures, Health
Effects and Public Policy, Proceedings of the 5th Annual CPHR
Symposium in Health Research & Policy, CPHR, Wellington, 2006.

45   M. Joy, 'The Environmental and Human Health Impacts of
Dairy Intensification: A Canterbury Case Study', VetScript,
September 2019, pp.32–35.

46   Ministry for the Environment and Stats NZ, Environment
Aotearoa 2019: New Zealand's Environmental Reporting Series,
Ministry for the Environment and Stats NZ, Wellington,
April 2019.

47   S. Hales, J. Atkinson, J. Metcalfe, G. Kuschel and A. Woodward,

'Long Term Exposure to Air Pollution, Mortality and Morbidity in New Zealand: Cohort Study', *The Science of the Total Environment*, 801 (2021), 149660, https://doi.org/10.1016/j.scitotenv.2021.149660 (accessed 19 January 2022).

48   Giles Parkinson, 'Tesla Boss Says Australia and NZ Car Fleets Are Dirty, and Killing People', The Driven, 8 April 2021, http://thedriven.io/2021/04/08/teslas-denholm-laments-dirty-car-fleets-in-nz-and-australia-and-pollution-death-toll (accessed 19 January 2022).

49   Skegg, *The Health of the People*.

50   P. O'Connor, *Rates of Reported Illness in Paritutu and Moturoa*, Taranaki District Health Board, New Plymouth, 2001; P. O'Connor, 'Community Responses', in H. Purnell, T. Slater, A. Eng and N. Pearce (eds), *Dioxin: Exposures, Health Effects and Public Policy*, Proceedings of the 5th Annual CPHR Symposium in Health Research & Policy, CPHR, Wellington, 2006; P. Shoemack, *Interim Report on Health Impact from Pentachlorophenol (PCPs) and Former Whakatane Sawmill Site*, District Health Board, Whakatane, 2001.

51   G. Durham, personal communication, 2021.

52   Jager et al., *Report of the Independent Taskforce on Workplace Health and Safety*.

53   Skegg, *The Health of the People*.

54   Ibid.

Appendix: A Short Introduction to Dioxin

1   A.H. Smith, 'Public Health Policy and Dioxin in the Environment', in H. Purnell, T. Slater, A. Eng and N. Pearce (eds), *Dioxin: Exposures, Health Effects and Public Policy*, Proceedings of the 5th Annual CPHR Symposium in Health Research & Policy, CPHR, Wellington, 2006.

2   Ibid.; A.H. Smith and P. Lopipero, *Evaluation of the Toxicity of Dioxins and Dioxin-Like PCBs: A Health Risk Appraisal for the New Zealand Population. A Report to the Ministry for the Environment*, Ministry for the Environment, Wellington, February 2001.

3   IARC Working Group on the Evaluation of Carcinogenic Risks to Humans, *IARC Monographs on the Evaluation of Carcinogenic Risks to Humans: Volume 69 – Polychlorinated Dibenzo-Para-Dioxins and Polychlorinated Dibenzofurans*, IARC, Lyon, 1997.

4   Smith, 'Public Health Policy and Dioxin in the Environment'.

Acknowledgements

I thank Aaron Blair, Gillian Durham, Amanda Eng, Laura Beane Freeman, David McLean, Andrea 't Mannetje, David Savitz, Phil Shoemack, David Skegg, Tania Slater, Allan Smith, Kurt Straif and Alistair Woodward for their comments on the draft manuscript. I thank Michael Baker, Gillian Durham, Amanda Eng, David McLean, David Skegg and Alistair Woodward for help with locating documents. Finally, I thank Shaun Hendy and Courtney Addison for their very helpful reviews, and Denis Welch for his excellent editing of the manuscript.

Neil Pearce, May 2022

About the Author

For over forty years Professor Neil Pearce has undertaken many significant public and occupational health studies, including a lead role in the Wellington research group that discovered the role of fenoterol in the New Zealand epidemic of asthma deaths. In 2011 he was appointed Professor of Epidemiology and Biostatistics at the London School of Hygiene and Tropical Medicine, following a previous role as Director of the Centre for Public Health Research in the Research School of Public Health on the Massey University Wellington Campus. He was a co-founder of the International Study of Asthma and Allergies in Childhood, which has evolved into the Global Asthma Network. Recently he has developed the DEGREE study of Chronic Kidney Disease of unknown cause, a disease prevalent in poor communities in Central America and South Asia. He is also involved in health and safety aspects of the European Space Agency/NASA Mars Sample Return Mission, which will bring back samples from Mars in the next decade.

About BWB Texts

BWB Texts are short books on big subjects from great New Zealand writers. They are succinct narratives spanning contemporary issues, memoir, history and science. With well over fifty BWB Texts in print and more available digitally, new works are published regularly. BWB Texts can be purchased from all good bookstores and online from www.bwb.co.nz.

BWB Texts include:

Fragments from a Contested Past: Remembrance, Denial and New Zealand History
Joanna Kidman, Vincent O'Malley, Liana MacDonald, Tom Roa and Keziah Wallis

Kārearea
Māmari Stephens

Kāinga: People, Land, Belonging
Paul Tapsell

He Pou Hiringa: Grounding Science and Technology in Te Ao Māori
Maria Amoamo, Merata Kawharu and Katharina Ruckstuhl (eds)

The History of a Riot
Jared Davidson

100% Pure Future: New Zealand Tourism Renewed
Sarah Bennett (ed.)

Two Hundred and Fifty Ways to Start an Essay about Captain Cook
Alice Te Punga Somerville

Living with the Climate Crisis: Voices from Aotearoa
Tom Doig (ed.)

The Platform: The Radical Legacy of the Polynesian Panthers
Melani Anae

Shouting Zeros and Ones: Digital Technology, Ethics and Policy in New Zealand
Andrew Chen (ed.)

Beyond These Shores: Aotearoa and the World
Nina Hall (ed.)

Imagining Decolonisation
Various

The Climate Dispossessed: Justice for the Pacific in Aotearoa?
Teall Crossen

Transforming the Welfare State: Towards a New Social Contract
Jonathan Boston

#NoFly
Shaun Hendy

Rebuilding the Kāinga: Lessons from Te Ao Hurihuri
Jade Kake

The Broken Estate: Journalism and Democracy in a Post-Truth World
Mel Bunce

Student Political Action in New Zealand
Sylvia Nissen

A Careful Revolution: Towards a Low-Emissions Future
David Hall (ed.)

The Health of the People
David Skegg

Still Counting
Marilyn Waring

Maui Street
Morgan Godfery

Mountains to Sea
Mike Joy (ed.)

Ko Taranaki Te Maunga
Rachel Buchanan

False Divides
Lana Lopesi

A Matter of Fact: Talking Truth in a Post-Truth World
Jess Berentson-Shaw

Better Lives: Migration, Wellbeing and New Zealand
Julie Fry and Peter Wilson

Doing Our Bit: The Campaign to Double the Refugee Quota
Murdoch Stephens

Thought for Food: Why What We Eat Matters
John D. Potter

Island Time: New Zealand's Pacific Futures
Damon Salesa

Portacom City: Reporting on the Christchurch and Kaikōura Earthquakes
Paul Gorman

The Ground Between: Navigating the Oil and Mining Debate in New Zealand
Sefton Darby

Sea Change: Climate Politics and New Zealand
Bronwyn Hayward

The Best of e-Tangata
Edited by Tapu Misa and Gary Wilson

Antibiotic Resistance: The End of Modern Medicine?
Siouxsie Wiles

Hopes Dashed?: The Economics of Gender Inequality
Prue Hyman

Safeguarding the Future: Governing in an Uncertain World
Jonathan Boston

The Stolen Island: Searching for 'Ata
Scott Hamilton

The Post-Snowden Era: Mass Surveillance and Privacy in New Zealand
Kathleen Kuehn

The Bike and Beyond: Life on Two Wheels in Aotearoa New Zealand
Laura Williamson

Late Love: Sometimes Doctors Need Saving as Much as Their Patients
Glenn Colquhoun

Three Cities: Seeking Hope in the Anthropocene
Rod Oram

Playing for Both Sides: Love Across the Tasman
Stephanie Johnson

Complacent Nation
Gavin Ellis

The First Migration: Māori Origins 3000BC – AD1450
Atholl Anderson

Silencing Science
Shaun Hendy

Going Places: Migration, Economics and the Future of New Zealand
Julie Fry and Hayden Glass

First published in 2022 by Bridget Williams Books Ltd
PO Box 12474, Wellington 6144, New Zealand
www.bwb.co.nz, info@bwb.co.nz.

ISBN 9781990046889 (Paperback), ISBN 9781990046858 (EPUB),
ISBN 9781990046865 (Kindle), ISBN 9781990046872 (PDF)
DOI https://doi.org/10.7810/9781990046889

A catalogue record for this book is available from the National
Library of New Zealand. Kei te pātengi raraunga o Te Puna
Mātauranga o Aotearoa te whakarārangi o tēnei pukapuka.

The publisher warmly acknowledges the significance of the ongoing
support provided by the Bridget Williams Books Publishing Trust.
The generous contribution from Ockham Residential for the
BWB Texts series is gratefully acknowledged. The commitment
of Creative New Zealand to good New Zealand publishing is also
acknowledged, and its support for this publication is appreciated.

Publisher: Tom Rennie
Editor: Denis Welch
Cover design: Neil Pardington Design
Internal design and typesetting: Katrina Duncan
Printer: Blue Star, Wellington